SHELLS

ACKNOWLEDGMENTS

The authors and publishers would like to thank the following for their help in the compilation of this book:
The National Museums of Scotland, Edinburgh: Geoffrey N. Swinney of the Department of Natural History; the former Head of Library, Manjil V. Mathew and his staff. The National Library of Scotland, Edinburgh: the Superintendent of Reference Services. Glasgow Museum and Art Gallery, Kelvingrove: Fred R. Woodward of the Department of Natural History. The Natural History Museum, London: the Head of Library Services, Rex Banks and his staff. The Linnean Society of London: the Council and Librarian, Gina Douglas. Reynolds House, Millbank, London: Tom Pain. Cavendish House, Carlisle: Robert Dance.

They would also like to thank the following for their kind permission to photograph the original prints in their possession:
The National Museums of Scotland, Edinburgh, for the plates appearing on pages 15, 19, 21, 33, 43, 45, 53, 57, 59, 63, 65, 67, 69, 73, 75, 77, 81, 83, 89, 93, 101, 103, 105, 107, 109, 111, 113, 117, 119, 121, 125. The Natural History Museum, London, for the plates appearing on pages 11, 13, 17, 23, 27, 49, 95, 115, 127. The National Library of Scotland, Edinburgh, for the plates appearing on pages 35, 37, 39, 51. The Linnean Society of London for the plates appearing on pages 25, 29, 31, 71, 99. Noel Gregory of Farnham Common, Bucks, for the plates appearing on pages 9, 47.

The remaining plates were provided by David Heppell (41, 61, 97, 123), S. Peter Dance (55, 85, 87, 91) and Studio Editions (79).

Classic Natural History Prints, *Shells*
published in 1991 by Studio Editions Ltd
Princess House, 50 Eastcastle Street
London W1N 7AP

Printed and bound in Italy

ISBN 1 85170 392 6

CLASSIC NATURAL HISTORY PRINTS

SHELLS

S. PETER DANCE
AND
DAVID HEPPELL

STUDIO EDITIONS
LONDON

INTRODUCTION 5

LIST OF PLATES

INTRODUCTION

Archaeological investigations in southern Europe and elsewhere have shown that shells were used for personal adornment thousands of years ago. At least fifteen hundred years before the Christian era, artists in Crete painted clay pots and jars with aesthetically pleasing figures of triton shells, murex shells and the Paper Nautilus. The Romans adopted the fluted shape of the scallop shell liberally in their public buildings and private dwellings, and the same motif is a familiar feature of Renaissance art and architecture.

From the early eighteenth century onwards, the influx of exotic objects from the East and West Indies spawned many "cabinets of curiosities" in Europe, especially in the Netherlands. In these private museums, shells had pride of place, valued for their beauty and rarity and often changing hands for large sums of money. The exploration of the Pacific in the eighteenth century and of the Americas, the Philippines, Japan and elsewhere in the nineteenth led to the discovery of thousands of previously unknown shells. A flood of publications describing and illustrating those discoveries poured from European and American presses, satisfying a growing demand for literature about shells – and incidentally providing most of the plates reproduced in this selection.

This preoccupation with shells shows their compelling fascination. Whether we simply pick up a few when on holiday or collect and study them seriously, few of us ignore them entirely. Yet we know little about their origins. When picked up empty on the beach, for instance, they are not obviously the external hard coverings of soft-bodied animals, such as oysters, mussels, cockles, whelks, winkles and snails, though anyone who has eaten these animals knows better.

Indeed it is not the shell but the animal within which is the common denominator of these creatures and all their relatives. Sea-slugs, creatures of great beauty, have no shells, neither have the much maligned octopuses, as a glance at the following plates will show, but they are related anatomically to oysters, mussels and the rest. For this reason the unfamiliar word "mollusc" (meaning "soft-bodied") is used to describe shell-bearing and related non-shell-bearing creatures alike. The study of molluscs and their shells is known as "conchology" ("malacology", an alternative term, has the same meaning); anything relevant to that study is "conchological" (or "malacological"), and a student of the subject is called a "conchologist" (or a "malacologist").

As molluscs comprise the second largest group of animals in the animal kingdom, it is not surprising that they are divided into different groups. The principal groups, all represented in these plates, are the gastropods (or univalves), including most molluscs with shells formed of one piece, coiled or uncoiled (the shell being often provided with a shelly or corneous plug, the operculum, which is attached to the animal and seals the aperture); the bivalves, having shells formed of two pieces, or valves; and the cephalopods, including squids and octopuses (without shells) and nautiluses.

Clearly there is great diversity among the creatures comprising the molluscan world. There is great diversity, too, in the artistic styles of those who prepared the following illustrations. For example there are the contrasts resulting from the passage of time. The first plate, from a book published in 1742, differs markedly from plates in nineteenth-century books. There are also stylistic and technical differences between the artwork published in different countries. Shell illustrations published in Germany and Britain, for example, are honestly executed though sometimes ponderous, rarely displaying the meticulous lines and delicate colouring of those published in France. The French, however, were inclined to portray shells whole and unblemished, delightful to look at but more like pieces of dress jewellery than natural objects which had been exposed to the elements. As several plates in this selection prove, they were also inclined to portray them upside-down (although they would argue that they were the right way up).

National characteristics apart, shells are among the most difficult of all natural objects for the artist to delineate, and in all ages they have tested the abilities of accomplished draughtsmen, such as John Ruskin, who pointed out that it required artistic skill of the highest order to portray them satisfactorily. The snail shell seen in one or two of Titian's pictures, Ruskin supposed, was introduced not as mere decoration but to show that Titian could paint anything he chose, even something as challenging as a snail shell. So wherein lies the artistic challenge of the shell of a snail or of any other mollusc? Unlike butterflies, birds, fish and some other creatures, many shells are seen to have unequal sides if split down the middle. Technically speaking they are bilaterally asymmetrical. Sometimes, because of this, the width of a pencil line separates a good drawing from an indifferent one. As William Swainson pointed out, early in the nineteenth century, "to delineate a shell with a proper degree of accuracy, as complete a knowledge of design, colouring and chiaro-scuro, is requisite, as in painting a cabinet picture of still life."

A knowledge of how a shell is constructed also helps. That may be why conchologists were responsible for so many of the original drawings upon which the illustrations reproduced here are based. Swainson himself was a superlatively talented artist, Thomas Brown a competent one; each of them illustrated his own works. Arthur Adams and most of the globe-trotting French conchologists captured in rapid watercolour sketches the ephemeral characteristics of living molluscan animals observed in the tropics. The Sowerbys, working as a team, produced thousands of engravings and lithographs of shells in the nineteenth century, many of them accompanying texts written by members of the same family. Wilhelm Kobelt and Wilhelm Dunker, German authors of innumerable publications about molluscs, provided most of their own illustrations; and the penultimate plate of this selection shows that Henry Augustus Pilsbry, the most prolific conchological author of them all, could also be his own artist.

Where did all the shells come from? Who collected them and why? Up to the second half of the eighteenth century the shells seen in the cabinets of European collectors were mostly from the Mediterranean, the coasts of western Europe and West Africa, the islands of the West Indies and the Indian Ocean. Dutch cabinets, as has been mentioned earlier, were augmented by natural objects brought from the East Indies, and for many years the most coveted shells came from that part of the world. Without wealth and status it was almost impossible to bring together a representative collection of shells, including those then considered rare and desirable. It helped if you were of royal blood, like Maria Theresa, Empress of Austria and mother of Marie Antoinette. Her fine collection, made entirely by purchase or gifts, was described by Baron von Born in a specially commissioned folio volume. One of Born's plates is reproduced here.

At that time, pitifully few books, among them a few select copies with their engraved plates coloured by hand, were available to help collectors identify shells. Then, as a result of the voyages of Captain Cook and other navigators, shells from the "South Seas" began arriving in Europe. Within a few short years the conchological scene was transformed. Thomas Martyn's *Universal Conchologist*, represented here by a plate portraying the Sunburst Star-shell from New Zealand, is a unique and exquisite record of the discoveries which brought about that transformation.

Once the French Revolution and the excesses of Napoleon had become history, further exploration of the Pacific and other oceans was possible. Exploratory vessels dispatched from France, Britain and other countries had men aboard who studied aspects of natural history and made collections of natural objects. The French sent Jean René Constant Quoy, Joseph Paul Gaimard and René Primevère Lesson. The British sent Charles Darwin, Richard Brinsley Hinds and Arthur Adams. These men, and others like them, collected molluscs wherever they went, accounts of their discoveries eventually appearing in scientific reports, often accompanied by hand coloured plates. Some of those plates are reproduced here, taken from reports of the voyages of the *Blossom*, the *Vénus* and the *Samarang*.

During the nineteenth century, however, the most significant additions to our knowledge of shells – and to the illustrated literature about them – was made not by government-sponsored expeditions and professional biologists but by amateur collectors. In the first half of the century the shell-collecting activities of one man in particular brought thousands of previously unknown shells to the attention of specialists who published descriptions and illustrations of them in journals and books. This man was Hugh Cuming, an Englishman of humble origins who devoted his life to conchology and spent several years collecting shells in exotic places, most notably in and around the Philippines. This extraordinary man distributed the shells he had collected far and wide, so that few collectors were without some of them. His huge collection made possible the larger publications of Lovell Augustus Reeve, in particular the twenty-volume *Conchologia Iconica*, and of George Brettingham Sowerby (2nd), notably the five-volume *Thesaurus Conchyliorum*.

Similarly the wealthy Baron Benjamin Delessert amassed a collection of shells which was used to illustrate several sumptuous publications, such as the multivolume *Species Général* of Louis Charles Kiener and the incomparable *Illustrations Conchyliologiques* of Jean Charles Chenu. Delessert, unlike Cuming, bought most of his shells but his purchases included several collections of historical importance, including that of the Chevalier de Lamarck, one of the great pioneers of conchology. A plate from Delessert's own impressive book, *Recueil de Coquilles décrites par Lamarck*, appears in this selection.

There is a noticeable difference between most of the shell plates published during the period spanning the eighteenth and early nineteenth centuries and those published later. The earlier plates often show shells grouped in a manner calculated to please the eye. The title of one of the books in which they appeared, for instance, is *Vergnügen der Augen und des Gemüths* (Delights for the Eyes and the Mind). This book also appeared in French and Dutch translations, and we include a plate from the latter in our selection. The author of the book, Georg Wolfgang Knorr, deliberately chose to make it visually appealing. The same is undoubtedly true of Franz Michael Regenfuss. His *Choix de Coquillages et de Crustacés*, with a surface area the size of a small coffee-table, has a dozen plates containing figures of shells which, though commonplace, were tastefully arranged and exquisitely coloured, as may be seen in the plate reproduced here.

From the mid-nineteenth century onwards, pictures in most shell books had a purely scientific, utilitarian function. It was no longer enough for them to be intellectually undemanding and easy on the eye; now they were meant to help specialists and serious collectors identify and classify shells. So we often see illustrations of shells regimented in rows, especially in publications which attempted to describe and compare many closely related species. Nevertheless some of the plates are pleasing to the eye, as the mulitiple images make satisfying compositions.

It has not been difficult for us to find attractive subjects in primarily scientific works; occasionally they even seem to show shells as art objects. Nicol's Cone, stranded on a sea-girt rock in James Wilson's *Illustrations of Zoology*, is a striking example of a supposedly new species treated in this way. So, too, is the beach-worn shell with its incrustation of worm shells soaring sky-wards in the plate taken from the report of the voyage of the *Vénus*. Heinrich Simroth's drawings of Alpine slugs – unpromising subjects surely – show that even creatures normally reviled may have an unsuspected beauty.

As far as living molluscs are concerned there can be no doubt that later representations of them are more satisfying, more lively, than earlier ones. The Areola Babylon at the centre of the plate showing shells collected on the voyage of the *Samarang* is more lifelike. But the Mexican glandina snail from the *Mission Scientifique au Mexique* is superb.

Most of the plates reproduced here were engraved or lithographed, but the final one reproduces a page of twentieth-century Japanese woodcuts, modern examples of an ancient art. A few of the original plates were coloured by printing processes developed during the nineteenth and twentieth centuries. These have not always been easy for us to distinguish from those coloured by hand.

"This is a very pleasing and curious department of natural history," says the anonymous author of the article on Conchology in the *Encyclopaedia Londinensis*, "for, in the infinite variety of shells dispersed over the universe, the hand of the Supreme Artist has displayed every graduation of beauty which can exist in a permanent form." It is a tribute to the artists, engravers and lithographers represented in this book that their work – much of it concealed in rare books that most people never see – captures that beauty so tellingly.

Horned Murex and other Gastropods (1742)

Purpura rectirostris major (now Horned Murex, *Bolinus cornutus*) (two larger figures) and others. Hand-coloured engraving by Pietro Antonio Pazzi from original drawings by Giuseppe Menabuoni, pl. 30 from N. Gualtieri's *Index Testarum Conchyliorum &c*, 1742. Size of plate 14½″ × 9½″.

During the first quarter of the seventeenth century, Niccolò Gualtieri was physician to Cosimo III, the Medici ruler of Tuscany, who had an interest in shells. It may have been to satisfy this interest that Gualtieri began to compile his folio book, although it was not published until nearly twenty years after Cosimo's death. The *Index Testarum Conchyliorum*, one of the pioneering books about conchology, is distinguished for its bold engravings, many showing shells resembling curiously shaped spinning-tops. Compared with most of the engravings reproduced in our book, these appear to show the shells upside down – a feature of shell illustration associated more particularly with books published in France. Although the book was not normally issued with the plates coloured, some copies were coloured later, presumably for the delectation of wealthy owners. The colourist of the plate reproduced here used a limited palette and showed a sublime disregard for accuracy, suggesting that the colouring is nearly as old as the book.

The large shell, shown here in two views, grows to a length of about six inches and is a conspicuous member of the West African fauna. The other spiky shell is the Purple Dye Murex, *Bolinus brandaris*, an important source of the purple dye used long ago by the Romans, the Phoenicians and other Mediterranean peoples. The colourist has made each shell redder than it is in nature. The central shell is the Snipe's Bill Murex, *Haustellum haustellum*, a common Indo-Pacific species which would have been highly prized in Gualtieri's day. The green coloration is fictitious; the shell is actually creamy white with brownish blotches.

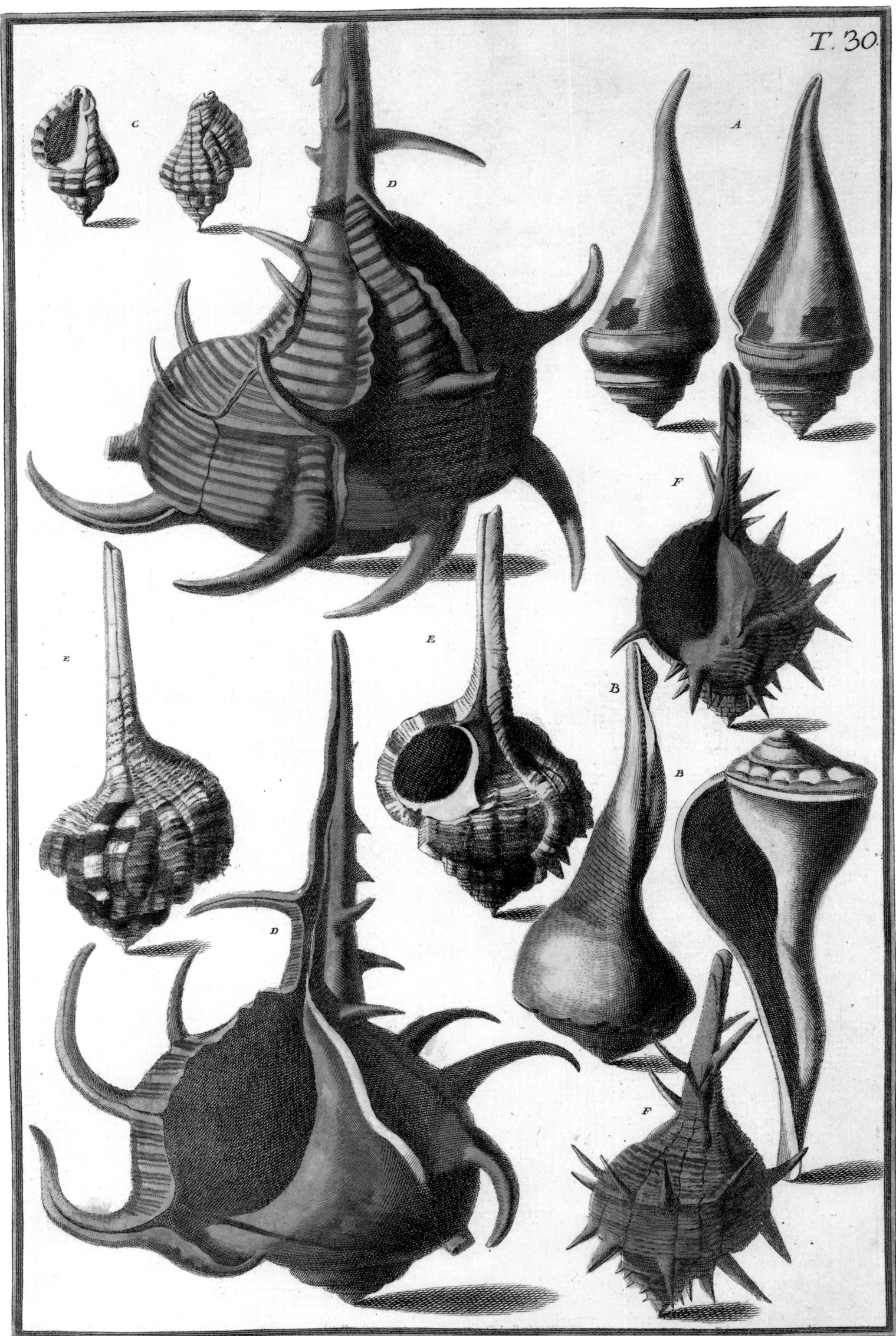

T. 30.

Turban Shells (1755)

TURBAN SHELLS (Turbinidae). Hand-coloured engraving by N.G. Geve, pl. 21 from his *Monatliche Belustigung im Reiche der Natur, an Conchylien und Seegewächsen*, 1755. Size of plate 9¼″ × 7″.

Nicolaus Georg Geve, a Hamburg artist, is not in the front rank of those who have advanced conchology but he has a small claim to distinction: he produced the first shell book issued with hand-coloured plates. This book, which began to appear in monthly parts in 1755, has always been one of the great rarities of conchological literature. Its impact on the science was negligible, however, as publication ceased after only 120 pages and thirty-three plates had been issued.

The illustrations on this plate are mostly of turban shells, common shells generally found about coral reefs in tropical waters. Geve showed here how colour and pattern vary from one example to another. Few species are more variable in these respects than some of the turban shells and none more so than the Tapestry Turban, *Turbo petholatus*, from the central and western Pacific (the larger shells on this plate). If Geve had shown such variations throughout the shell world, as seems to have been his intention, his book would have extended to several volumes and would have been a major contribution to conchology.

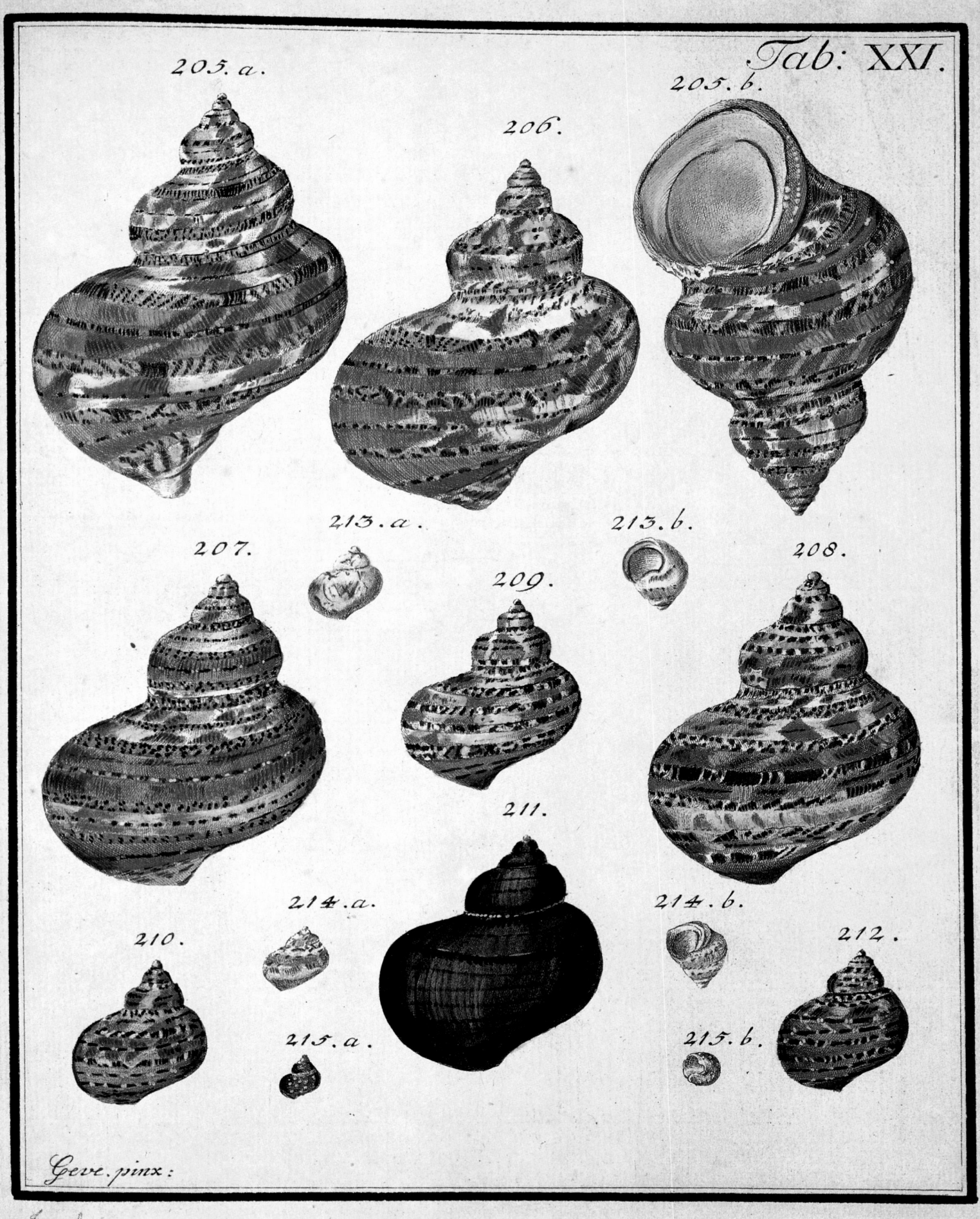

Tab: XXI

205. a.   206.   205. b.

207.   213. a.   213. b.   208.

209.

210.   214. a.   211.   214. b.   212.

215. a.   215. b.

Geve. pinx:

Turbo

Seba's Spider-conch and Others (1758)

ALATA LATA (now Seba's Spider-conch, *Lambis truncata sebae*) (two larger central figures) and others. Hand-coloured engraving, pl. 63 from Vol. 3 (1758) of A. Seba's *Locupletissimi Rerum Naturalium Thesauri Accurata Descriptio &c*, 1734–65. Size of plate 16½″ × 10½″.

During the early eighteenth century, the wealthier inhabitants of Amsterdam and other large cities in the Netherlands deployed some of their wealth in the purchase of natural and artificial objects. A well-stocked curiosity cabinet could be a status symbol, and often a collector would spend more on a rare shell or a stuffed bird than he would on a painting by a renowned artist. Dealers in such things plied a flourishing trade, and often the supply could not satisfy the demand. Albertus Seba, an Amsterdam apothecary, was one of the more energetic and omnivorous of these Dutch connoisseurs. Having sold a collection to Peter the Great of Russia he speedily amassed another, larger one and commissioned various "scientific men" to describe and illustrate it. In what is now often known as Seba's *Thesaurus*, his entire second collection was described and illustrated.

The third volume is largely devoted to his extensive collection of shells. Here we see a few, most of them known as spider conchs, in allusion to the finger-like projections around the outer edge of the aperture of adult specimens; those shown here are all immature and so the projections are lacking. The two large figures in the centre represent the immature form of a shell which may be more than a foot long when mature. Named Seba's Spider-conch, because it was first made known by these illustrations, it is a common shell in the tropical Pacific Ocean. Like all the other shells on this plate, it is incorrectly depicted back to front: the aperture should be at the right-hand side. The engraver forgot to engrave the figures in mirror image so that when a print was taken from the engraved metal plate all the figures were reversed – a mistake often repeated in shell books illustrated with engravings.

TAB. LXIII.

Green Turban and other Tropical Shells (1758)

OREILLE DE GÉANT (now Green Turban, *Turbo marmoratus*) (second row, two outer figures) and other Tropical Shells. Hand-coloured engraving, pl. 5 from F.M. Regenfuss's *Choix de Coquillages et de Crustacés &c*, 1758. Size of plate 16½″ × 11″.

In 1748 the German artist and engraver Franz Michael Regenfuss extolled the virtues of shell collecting and invited subscriptions for a publication which was to contain a scientific text and many illustrations. Ten years later, with the help of Danish royalty and nobility, the *Choix de Coquillages* was published, the text (written by Christian Gottlieb Kratzenstein) being printed in French and German, the twelve plates having been engraved from the author's own drawings and coloured mostly by his wife. The book was an immediate success, the composition and colouring of the plates and their sheer size – in surface area it exceeds all other books devoted exclusively to shells – making it a luxurious and exclusive production. Undoubtedly the *Choix de Coquillages* was intended to satisfy the eyes as much as the minds of those who purchased it.

Speaking about the Green Turban, the author says "They are generally found with a calcareous crust, particularly the larger ones. This can be scraped off or dissolved by aqua fortis [nitric acid], after which the shells should be washed. The Chinese, with whom this snail is found in great abundance, cut off the second whorl close to the mouth, then they grind the shell all around the middle down to nacre, leaving four small projections as feet, and sell them as salt cellars to the Europeans . . . It occurs in China, Java and other places in the East Indies in large quantities. It keeps to the shores where steep rocky coast prevails, which makes fishing difficult; but where they occur they do so in large quantities." Because of the difficulty of getting together fine and rare specimens, scattered in various private collections, Regenfuss did not attempt to arrange his figures in any systematic order, as he wanted his plates to be published without delay. Although he had completed original drawings for a second volume and part of a third, which he intended to bring out as soon as engravings of them could be coloured, no further parts were ever published.

FIG. 49.   TAB. V.

FIG. 50.   FIG. 50.

FIG. 52.   FIG. 51.   FIG. 52.

FIG. 53.

FIG. 54.   FIG. 54.

FIG. 56.   FIG. 56.

FIG. 55.

FIG. 57.   FIG. 57.

FIG. 49.

FIG. 58.   FIG. 58.

Ear Shells (1771)

EAR SHELLS, Haliotidae. Hand-coloured engraving by P. Mazell from original drawings by P. Brown, pl. 9 from E.M. da Costa's *Conchology, or Natural History of Shells*, 1771. Size of plate 12″ × 8½″.

The activities of Emanuel Mendes da Costa, a versatile fossilist and conchologist, comprise one of the more intriguing chapters of eighteenth-century natural history. Elected Clerk to the Royal Society in 1763, he was accused of misappropriating the Society's funds and was imprisoned in 1768. He emerged from prison in 1772, having spent some of his time there working on his *Conchology*, from which this picture has been taken. While writing this book he was helped in various ways by George Humphrey, then London's best-known shell dealer.

The shells illustrated in this plate are all ear shells (or abalones). They belong to a family widely distributed in the world's oceans, their ear-shaped shells being characteristic. The two bottom figures show the Midas Ear-shell, *Haliotis midae*, a common South African species. The three top figures represent the Ass's Ear, *Haliotis asinina*, a species widespread in the south-western Pacific.

Some of Peter Brown's original watercolour drawings for the *Conchology*, including this one, are now in the Natural History Museum in London. Painted on sheets of vellum (prepared calfskin), they have a much more delicate finish than the published engravings. To da Costa, languishing in prison, Peter Brown's paintings must have seemed like sunbeams. The engravings Peter Mazell made from them comprise most of da Costa's unfinished book, as the text accompanying them is fragmentary. Perhaps even his four years of imprisonment left da Costa, who has been dubbed the "wayward Hebrew genius", with insufficient time for conchology.

Plate IX.

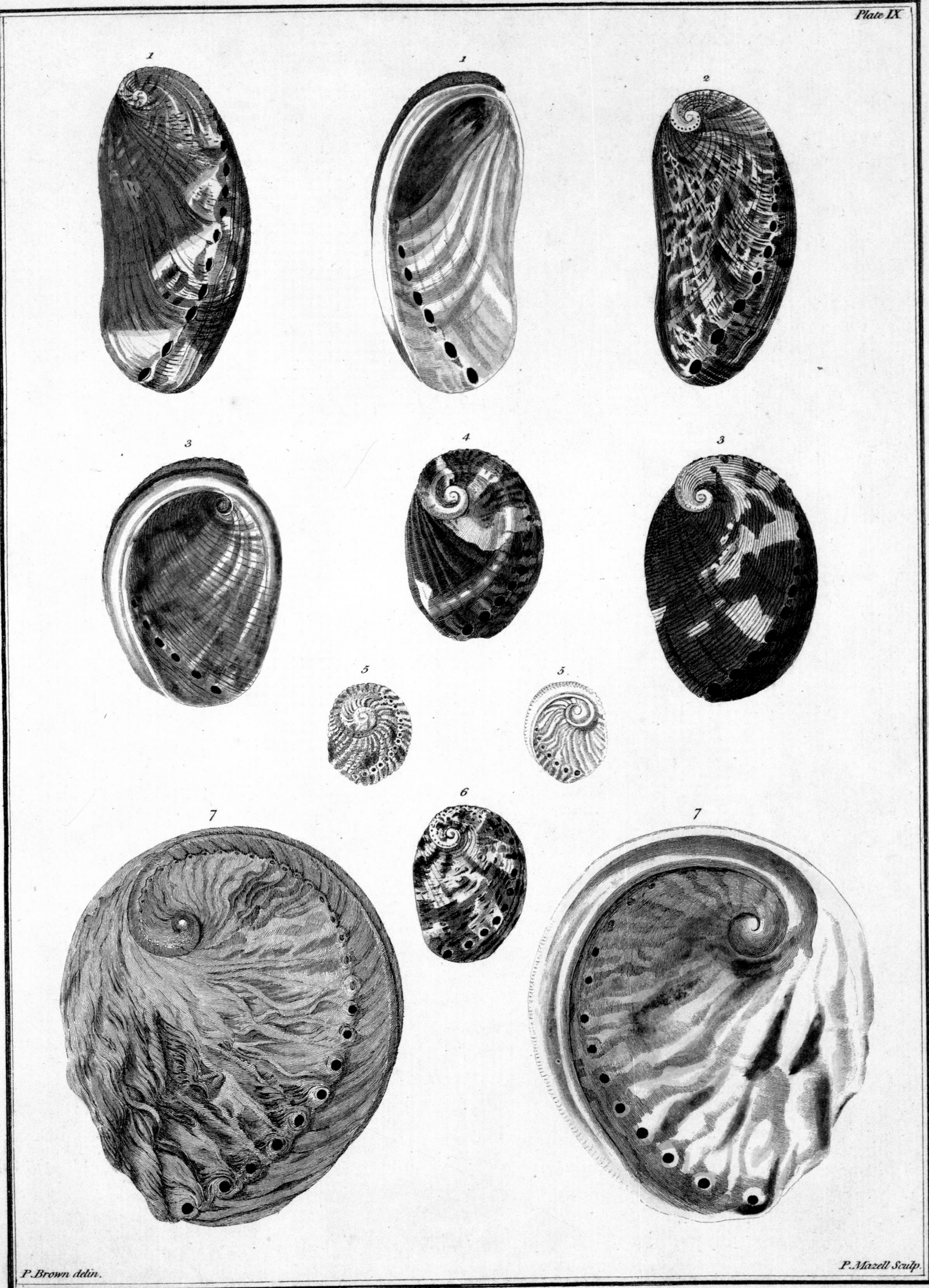

Matchless Cone and other Cone Shells (1775)

CEDO NULLI (now Matchless Cone, *Conus cedonulli*) (centre) and other Cone Shells. Hand-coloured engraving by Gustav Philipp Trautner, pl. 1 from Part 6 (1775) of G.W. Knorr's *Verlustiging der Oogen en van den Geest &c*, 1770–5. Size of plate 8″ × 6¼″.

The title of Georg Wolfgang Knorr's book about shells may be translated as "Delights for the Eyes and the Mind", and the attractive plates give meaning to that title. The accompanying text does little more than supply additional information about the appearance of the shells, but as the book appeared in German, French and Dutch it must have had wide popular appeal.

Occupying the centre of the plate is the most coveted shell of the eighteenth century: the Matchless Cone, *Conus cedonulli*. The specimen depicted here was the pride and joy of Pierre Lyonet, whose shell collection in The Hague was one of the largest and finest in the Netherlands. So enamoured of this West Indian shell was he that he seldom allowed anyone to see it. Sometimes, however, he allowed an artist to paint a delicate study of it for the benefit of an envious collector. The figure published by Knorr had to be copied from such a painting. Albertus Seba, the Amsterdam apothecary and connoisseur of natural curiosities, commissioned a miniaturist to paint Lyonet's specimen and was allowed to examine it himself. "While I had this beautiful piece in my hand and could look at it closely," he says, "I was disturbed by the remarkable beauty and the pattern of all sorts of colours and ornaments which it possesses."

Judging by Knorr's engraving, Seba's comment may seem unwarranted, but there was a mystique about this species then, probably fostered by Lyonet's protective attitude to his specimen, which was infectious. When Lyonet's shell was sold at the auction of his collections of natural curiosities and art objects in 1796, it fetched 273 Dutch guilders. During the same auction Vermeer's *Woman in Blue Reading a Letter* made forty-three guilders. It may seem incredible that a picture now considered priceless could then have made much less than a shell worth about the price of a good meal for two in 1990, but so it was. The story of the Matchless Cone shows how time and caprice may influence our appreciation of the rare and the beautiful in nature and art.

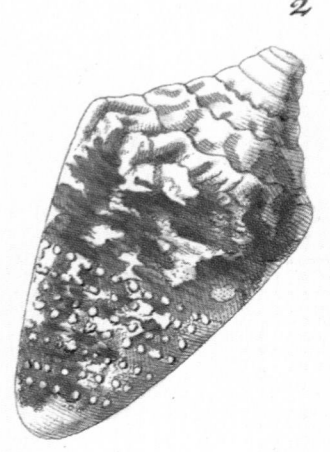

2

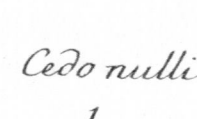

3

Cedo nulli

1

4

5

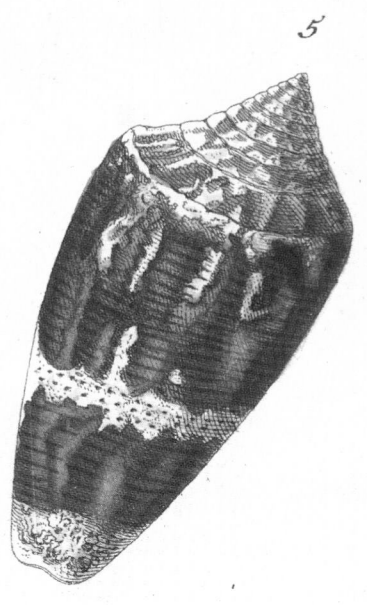

Fig. 2–5, Ex Museo Houttuyniano.

G. P. Trautner sculpsit.

Swan Mussel (1779)

GRÖSSTE FLACHE GRÜNGESTRAHLTE TEICHMUSCHEL (now Swan Mussel, *Anodonta cygnea*) (centre). Hand-coloured engraving by J.S. Capieux from life, pl. 1 from J.S. Schröter's *Geschichte der Flussconchylien & c*, 1779. Size of plate 8¾″ × 7″.

Johann Samuel Schröter, Deacon of the parish of St Peter and St Paul in Weimar, was an enthusiastic naturalist. Curator of the ducal collections of Nature and Art, he was also a member of several scientific academies and of the society for the study of the physical economy of honey bees. This illustration is from his encyclopaedic *Geschichte der Flussconchylien* (History of River Shells). In his Preface he explains, with no false modesty, that he gave his book that title because in it he had brought together everything anyone should know about river shells if they wished to have a complete knowledge of the subject. Certainly the book was as complete as he could make it, having worked on it for thirteen years. His studies of specimens from the ponds and rivers of Thuringia, supplemented by a widespread correspondence and the published accounts of his predecessors, resulted in what he considered to be a comprehensive account of the freshwater shells of the world.

The drawings for the plates were made in Weimar by the artist Johann Stephan Capieux under Schröter's direct supervision. The large specimen shown here measured 8¾″ × 5½″ and was estimated to be between twelve and sixteen years old. It was taken from the Schwansee, a sizeable lake in the Duchy of Eisenach. Schröter believed it to be distinct from the Swan Mussel, *Anodonta cygnea*, but did not give it a new scientific name. It is now recognized as merely a rather flat variety of that species, characteristic of some lakes. The two smaller figures on the same plate represent river forms of the Duck Mussel, *Anodonta anatina*.

Tab. I.

Schröters Fluſs = Conchyl.

2.

1.

3.

a

Capieux ad natur del & sculp. 1779.

Maria Theresa's Cornucopia and Others (1780)

Cornu copiae (now the "Cornucopia" monstrosity of the Common Snail, *Helix aspersa*) (lower corners) and others. Hand-coloured engraving by Carl Schütz, pl. 13 from I. von Born's *Testacea Musei Caesarei Vindobonensis*, 1780. Size of plate 14½" × 10¼".

After years of conflict, including the Seven Years' War, Maria Theresa, Empress of Austria, devoted her considerable energies to peaceful activities such as founding schools and charitable societies. She also took an interest in natural curiosities and amassed a considerable collection of them, now preserved in the Natural History Museum in Vienna. Ultimately the collection was considered important enough for her to command Baron Ignaz von Born to describe it, which he did in a modest volume published in 1778. Two years later Born produced a more impressive book in which many of the conchological treasures of the imperial collection were well illustrated in colour.

The shells shown in this plate from the later book represent an equal mixture of marine and non-marine species and are so well drawn that almost every one of them is identifiable. Of particular interest is the "Cornucopia", the shell occupying the two lower corners. This was considered one of the great rarities of the collection. At the time it was the only one of its kind known anywhere. Described by Born as *Cornu copiae*, it is a pathological form of the Common Snail, *Helix aspersa*, in which the shell is competely unwound. Such extreme monstrosities of this abundant species are very rare. A coloured engraving of it comprises the frontispiece to Born's 1778 work. The *Testacea Musei Caesarei Vindobonensis* is still important to conchologists because it contains descriptions of several new species.

Tab. 13.

Maculated Dwarf-triton and Others (1780)

GEFLEKTE KINKHORN, *Buccinum maculosum* (now Maculated Dwarf-triton, *Colubraria muricata*) (top right and top left) and others. Hand-coloured engraving, probably by Johann Sebastian Leitner, from original drawings by Johann Friedrich August Krüger, pl. 132 from Vol. 4 (1780) of F.H.W. Martini and J.H. Chemnitz's *Neues Systematisches Conchylien-Cabinet &c*, 1769–95. Size of plate 9¼″ × 7½″.

Friedrich Wilhelm Martini, a Hamburg physician, conceived the idea of publishing the first large-scale encyclopaedia of shells illustrated with hand-coloured engravings. His ambition was to describe and portray every kind of shell known, an ambition virtually impossible to fulfil, as others have discovered since. No sooner was the third volume of the *Neues Systematisches Conchylien-Cabinet* in print than its author died, in 1778. Publication was continued by Johann Hieronymus Chemnitz, a Danish clergyman who, between 1779 and 1795, added a further eight volumes.

Incomplete though it was, the book did provide a much-needed collection of illustrated shell descriptions and was an invaluable reference source for many years. Its illustrations, as is obvious from this plate, were not conspicuously superior to those published previously but they were arranged more systematically – and there were plenty of them. The original drawings of the Maculated Dwarf-triton, illustrated here at top left and top right, were taken from a shell in Chemnitz's own collection. The other illustrations represent a mixture of two species, the Robin Redbreast Triton, *Cymatium rubeculum*, and the Black-striped Triton, *Cymatium hepaticum*, also based on shells in the Chemnitz collection. In 1780 these two species were treated as one. Like the Maculated Dwarf-triton, both occur around coral reefs in the Indian and Pacific oceans.

Tab. CXXXII.

Knotige Kinkhörner.
Buccina 2, nodosa.

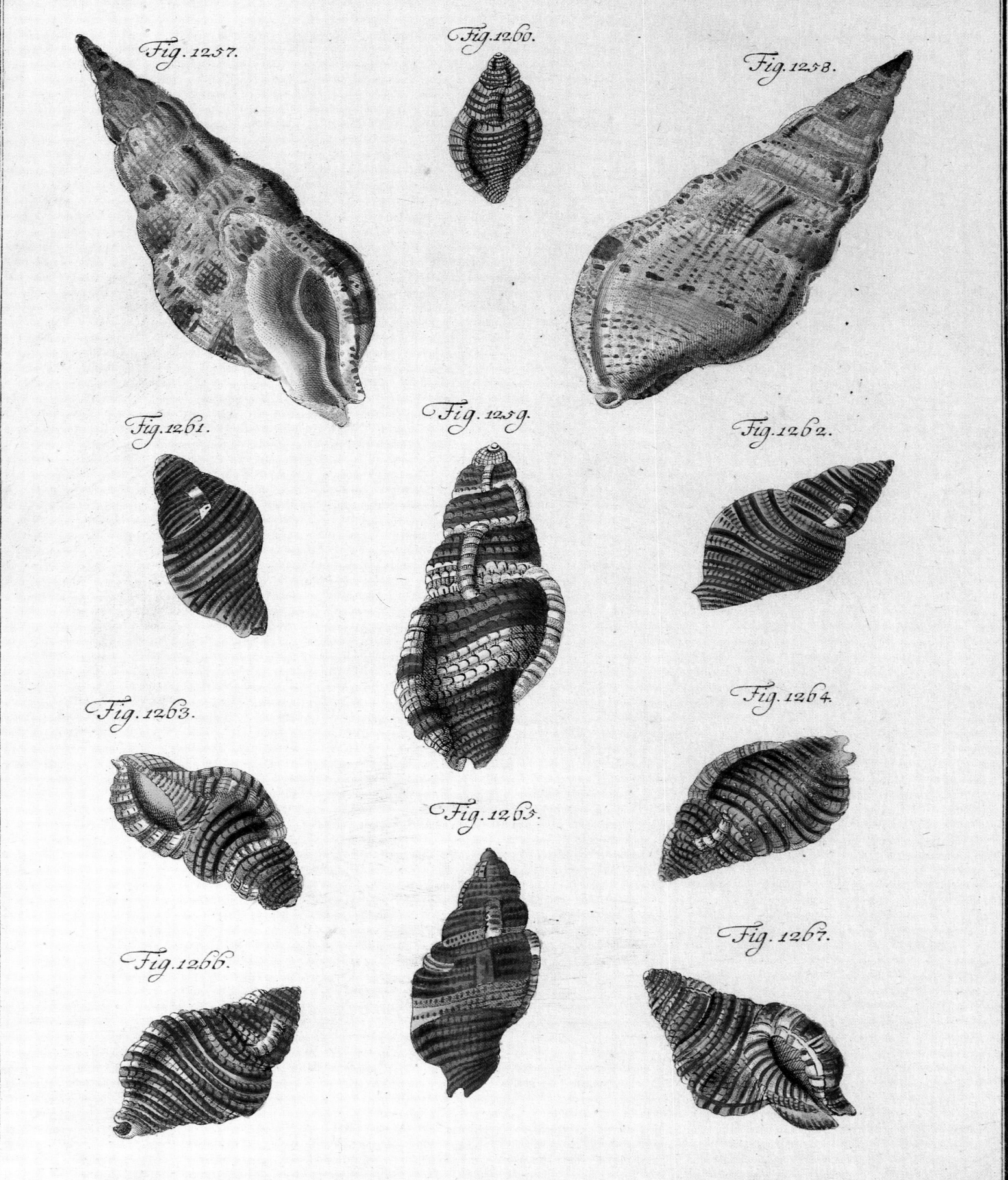

Fig. 1257.

Fig. 1260.

Fig. 1258.

Fig. 1261.

Fig. 1259.

Fig. 1262.

Fig. 1263.

Fig. 1264.

Fig. 1265.

Fig. 1266.

Fig. 1267.

Sarmatian Snail and Exotic Shells (1782)

Cochlea Sarmatica (now Sarmatian Snail) (fourth row, right-hand shell) and Exotic Shells. Hand-coloured engraving, pl. 32 from Vol. 2 of J.A. Battara's edition of F. Buonanni's *Rerum Naturalium Historia &c*, 1782. Size of plate 10″ × 6½″.

This plate first appeared in 1709 in the first edition of *Rerum Naturalium Historia*, a book describing and illustrating the curiosities bequeathed in 1680 to the College of the Society of Jesus in Rome by Athanasius Kircher, a Jesuit. Except for the application of limited colouring, the plates of shells in this late-eighteenth-century version of the book scarcely differ from those of the 1709 edition. Its original author, Filippo Buonanni, has a special significance for us because he wrote the earliest treatise exclusively devoted to conchology. He succeeded Kircher as Professor of Mathematics at the College in 1680, and a year later published his pioneering work on conchology, *Ricreatione dell' Occhio e della Mente*, illustrated with engravings of Kircher's shells. Versions of many of the engravings appear again in his *Rerum Naturalium Historia*.

The engravings, noticeably cruder in their execution than others dating from the late eighteenth century, mostly represent species likely to be present in a collection formed during the seventeenth century. One of them, however, represents a creature which was never one of Kircher's curiosities. Said to be from the Sarmatian Sea (the Black Sea), it is the Sarmatian Snail, here incongruously occupying the middle of the plate. A version of the engraving occurs in a book published in 1573 by Ambroise Paré, the so-called "Father of French surgery".

A 1649 English translation of Paré's book says that this creature, which resembles a snail, "equal's a barrell in magnitude of bodie, and a stag in the largeness and branches of her horns: the ends of her horns are rounded as it were into little balls, shineing like unto pearls." It was supposed to have four legs and a long tail which enabled it to swim. Altogether the Sarmatian Snail was a very ugly creature. Paré said someone had seen it in Denmark.

The shells illustrated on the same plate are mostly examples of common species found on either side of the Atlantic.

Various Gastropods and Bivalves (1787)

GASTROPODS AND BIVALVES. Hand-coloured engraving by Moses Harris, pl. 97 from Vol. 2 of W.F. Martyn's *New Dictionary of Natural History; or Compleat Universal Display of Animated Nature*, 1784–7. Size of plate 13″ × 7½″.

This plate pleases the eye because it consists of simple shapes disposed without any obvious striving after artistic effect. It is taken from a little-known dictionary (it would now be called an encyclopaedia) wherein its main function was probably to add a splash of colour. One of the earliest surveys of natural history to deal with its subjects in alphabetical order, the *New Dictionary* is still valuable as a quick reference for historians of science. The artist responsible for this plate (and nine others in the book) was Moses Harris, author and illustrator of *The Aurelian*, among the most celebrated and most beautiful of all books about butterflies and moths.

William Frederic Martyn, compiler of the *New Dictionary*, was not an authority on molluscs and their shells. This plate is captioned "Univalves", meaning gastropods, or shells formed of one piece, but the bottom right-hand and bottom-centre figures show bivalve (or two-piece) shells. No matter – we are not looking for scientific correctness: discovering this delightful plate in an obscure eighteenth-century dictionary is rewarding enough.

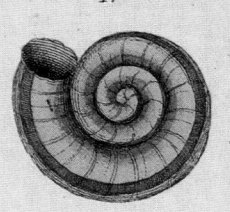

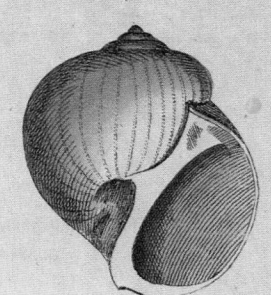

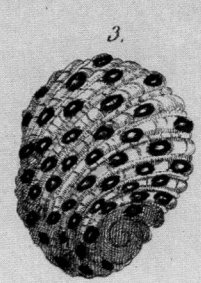

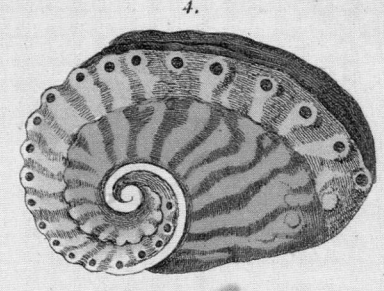

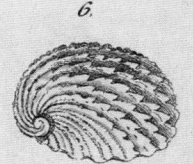

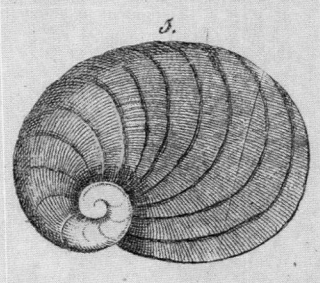

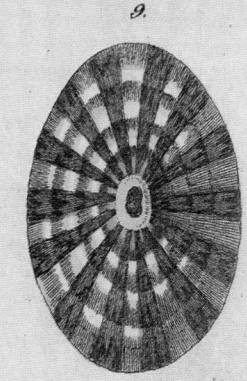

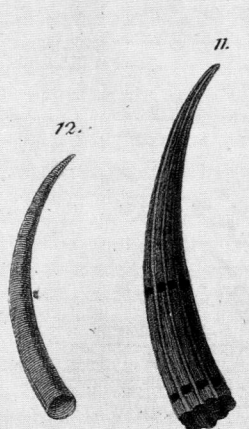

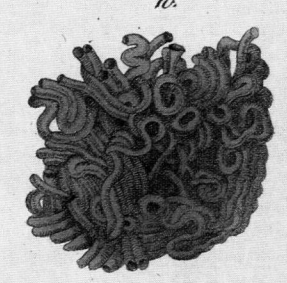

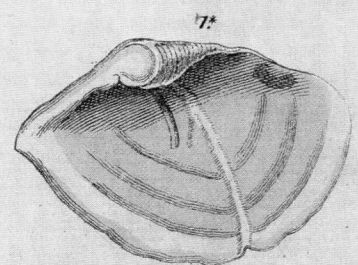

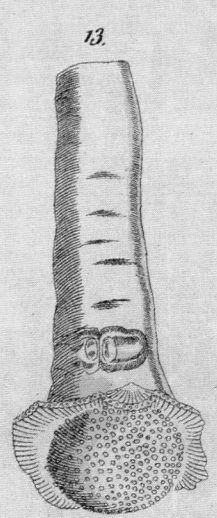

PLATE I.* UNIVALVES.

1. RAM'S HORN SNAIL.	6. CHAMBERED LIMPET.	10. WORM-TUBES.
2. SHORT-TURBANED SNAIL.	7. GOAT'S EYE LIMPET.	11. GREEN-TOOTH-SHELL.
3. MAGPIE NERITE.	8. COMMON LIMPET.	12. BROWN-TOOTH-SHELL.
4. EAR-SHELL.	9. MASKED LIMPET.	13. WATERING-POT-SHELL.
5. WHITE EAR-SHELL.		

MULTIVALVE.

1.* PHOLAS.

Plate XCVII.

Published as the Act directs by Harrison and Cº March 1ª 1787.

Moses Harris del et sc

Shells from the Cook Voyages (1788)

SHELLS from the Cook voyages. Hand-coloured engraving, possibly by Georg Vogel, pl. 169 from Vol. 10 (1788) of F.H.W. Martini and J.H. Chemnitz's *Neues systematisches Conchylien-Cabinet &c*, 1769–95. Size of plate 10″ × 7½″.

There were two main reasons why the *Neues systematisches Conchylien-Cabinet* could not have been made into a complete illustrated inventory of shells. Even if the thousands of species added to science in the nineteenth and twentieth centuries are excluded from the reckoning, there was already a daunting number of species known when the book was begun; and further collections of shells, including many unfamiliar species, were beginning to filter into Europe as a result of explorations in the Pacific and elsewhere. The exploratory voyages superintended by James Cook to lands in the "South Seas" were particularly fruitful, and many remarkable species found their way into collectors' cabinets, particularly in Britain. In Copenhagen, Chemnitz purchased examples of some of the newly discovered shells from dealers in other countries, to describe and illustrate in the later volumes of his great work, but for many he had to rely on figures provided by Thomas Martyn in the first edition of *The Universal Conchologist*. Some of the shells on this plate were copied from that work.

The shells illustrated here were probably all associated with one or other of the Cook voyages into the Pacific. At the centre of the plate is the Common Northwest Neptune, *Neptunea lyrata*, a species which occurs from northern California to the Arctic. The specimen was brought back to England from Vancouver Island by someone who travelled with Captain Cook on his third and last voyage, which had been completed, minus its leader, in 1780. In the bottom corners of the plate we see figures of the Lightning Moon-turban, *Subninella undulata*, from South Australia. A Polynesian species, the Prismatic Latirus, *Latirus iris*, occupies the upper corners; when wetted its outer skin becomes iridescent, a property which made it popular among collectors for a few years.

Fig.1635.

Fig.1639.

Fig. 1636.

Fig.1642.

Fig. 1634.

Fig.1644.

Fig.1645.

Fig.1646.

Fig.1637.

Fig. 1638.

Fig.1641.

Fig.1640

Fig. 1643.

Sunburst Star-shell (1789)

SUN TROCHUS, *Trochus heliotropium* (now Sunburst Star-shell, *Astraea heliotropium*). Hand-coloured stipple engraving, pl. 30 from Vol. 1 of the second edition of T. Martyn's *Universal Conchologist*, 1789. Size of plate 13½″ × 10″.

In October 1780 the vessels *Resolution* and *Discovery* returned to England after the third and final voyage of exploration conducted by Captain James Cook, who had been killed during the voyage. A dealer named Thomas Martyn lost no time buying from the crews of the ships all the shells he could get his hands on. His objective was not to sell them for a profit but to choose from among them specimens to serve as models for drawings from which engravings could be made for an ambitious publishing venture. The conchological novelties brought from the Pacific by the men who sailed with Cook were so different from the familiar shells of the West Indies, the Mediterranean, West Africa and other parts of the world that he wanted to make them the exclusive subjects of a lavishly illustrated book, *The Universal Conchologist*.

As he could not obtain as many previously unknown shells as he had anticipated, each of his plates shows only a single species, usually in two views. The task of drawing the chosen specimens Martyn entrusted to "young persons who, born of good but humble parents, could not from their own means aspire to the cultivation of any liberal art, at the same time as they gave indications of natural talent for drawing and design". These young persons formed Martyn's little academy, and within a few years they were proficient enough to put his plan into effect. *The Universal Conchologist*, which eventually amounted to 160 plates in four folio volumes issued between 1784 and 1787. It took its place on the bookshelves of discerning and wealthy patrons and became one of the most celebrated of all conchological publications.

At their best the illustrations are excellent and received high praise, but Martyn himself was dissatisfied, as "the more early performances appeared so very inferior to the later". The unsold copies, the engraved plates, and even the original paintings were rejected after about seventy copies of the first eighty plates had been completed, and the whole work was begun anew "in that improved style of execution which was ultimately to determine the fate and reputation of the work". A second edition of these plates was published in 1789, in a slightly reduced format. The most striking of them may be this one of a Sunburst Star-shell shown from above and below. This New Zealand species, introduced to science by Martyn, was one of the most outstanding conchological discoveries made during the Cook voyages, and collectors snapped up specimens eagerly.

The Amours of Snails (1790)

GARDEN SNAIL (now Common Snail, *Helix aspersa*). Hand-coloured engraving by F.P. Nodder, pl. 30 from Vol. 1 (1789–90) of G. Shaw and F.P. Nodder's *Naturalist's Miscellany &c*, 1789–1813. Size of plate 7½″ × 4½″.

Frederick Polydore Nodder, Botanic Painter to Queen Charlotte, began a popular monthly series of coloured illustrations in 1789 under the title *Vivarium Naturae, or the Naturalist's Miscellany*. After Frederick's death his widow Elizabeth continued the publication, helped by their son Richard Polydore, who was responsible for the engravings. Most of the 1,068 plates issued in the twenty-four annual volumes show birds, insects, fish and molluscs.

The accompanying text was written by George Shaw, one of the founders of the Linnean Society and Keeper of the Natural History Section at the British Museum. In his description of the Garden Snail, Shaw refutes the "ingenious hypothesis" that the snail's horns are a kind of natural telescope which the animal can shorten or lengthen according to the distance of the object in view. But in his account of the snail's courtship, the subject of Nodder's engraving, he surprisingly perpetuates the popular fallacy that "When these animals are disposed to love, they signify their mutual wishes by launching several little darts at each other." The lyrical details of "the amours of Snails" provided here are, unfortunately, more romantic than scientific. The snails' behaviour before mating has all the appearance of an elaborate and often protracted courtship ritual in which the darts do play a part but, unlike Cupid's darts, they are not projected from afar. To be fair to Shaw, he does admit that the snails are shown at too great a distance from each other.

Paper Nautilus Sailing (1792)

ARGONAUT, or Paper Nautilus, *Argonauta argo*. Hand-coloured engraving by F.P. Nodder, pl. 101 from Vol. 3 (1791–2) of G. Shaw and F.P. Nodder's *Naturalist's Miscellany &c*, 1789–1813. Size of plate 6¾″ × 5″.

The animal which lives in the Paper Nautilus shell puzzled George Shaw as much as it had earlier zoologists. The shell appeared to be that of a univalve mollusc, while its inhabitant closely resembled an octopus, which lacks any vestige of a shell. Arguments about whether the Argonaut animals, like hermit crabs, merely occupied vacant shells, had not been finally settled. We now know that the Paper Nautilus is really an exquisitely formed case within which the female Argonaut guards and nurtures her eggs. The male Argonaut is a dwarf and has no shell.

As Shaw noted, the main difference between the Argonaut animal and octopus-like creatures was that two of the Argonaut's arms were modified at their tips to form a pair of oval membranes. These are the two arms which secrete and cradle the shell, but their function was unknown to Shaw and his contemporaries. As a result, the age-old story of the Argonaut's ability to sail on the surface of a calm sea was given credence anew. The narrative tells how "it raises upright and expands to the gale" the specially adapted arms as a sail, "while by the assistance of the six remaining arms it rows itself along". In this way the Argonaut "pursues its voyage like a little ship; and, if alarmed by any appearance of danger, takes in water and descends".

The Argonaut lives in the Mediterranean and tropical seas. Its fabled sailing was regarded in classical times as among the principal miracles of Nature, a charming notion which took a long time to die out. Although Frederick Polydore Nodder's illustrations were claimed to be "drawn and described immediately from Nature", this plate owes its origin to a venerable but false tradition.

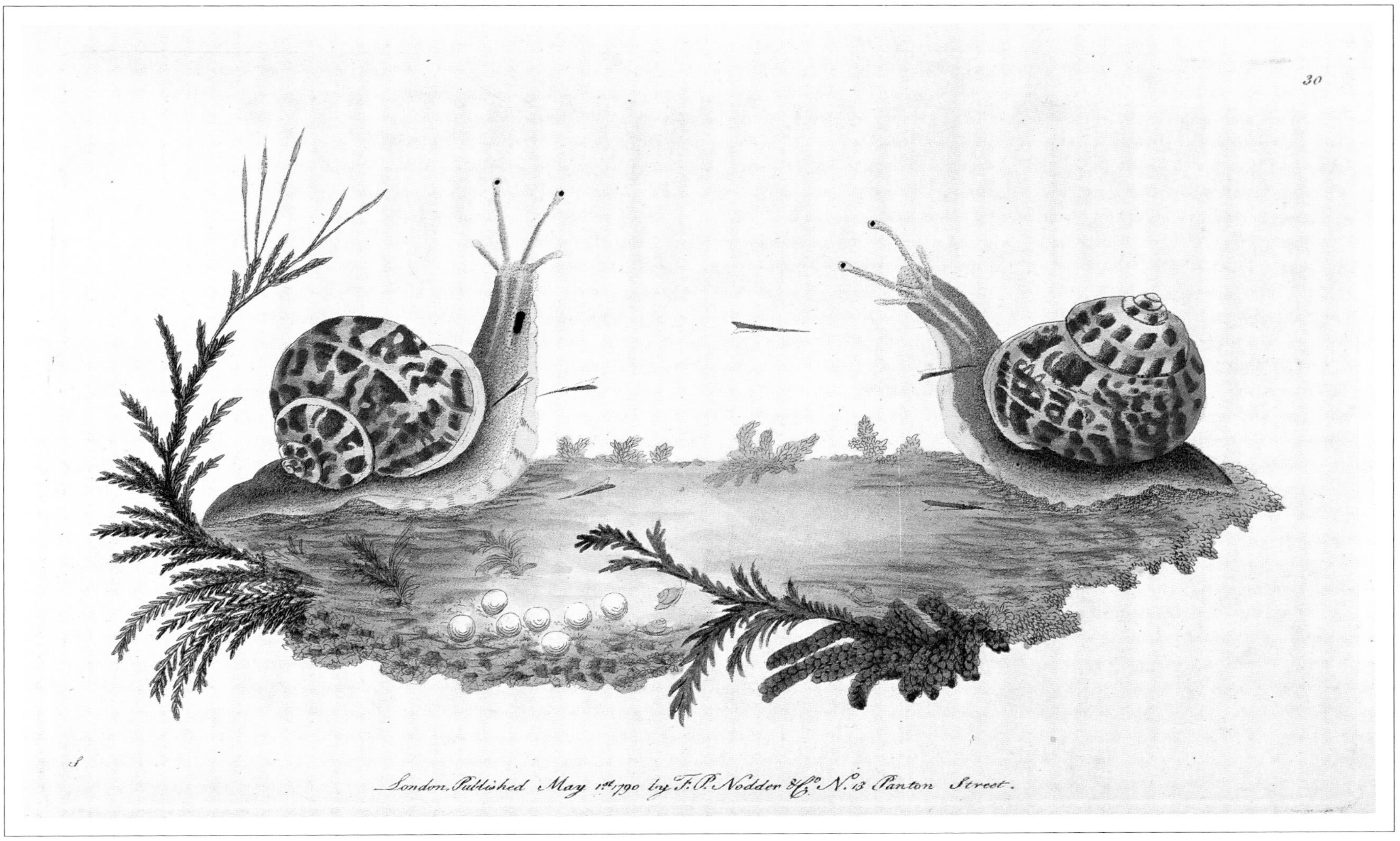
30
S
London, Published May 1st 1790 by F. P. Nodder & Co. No. 13 Panton Street.

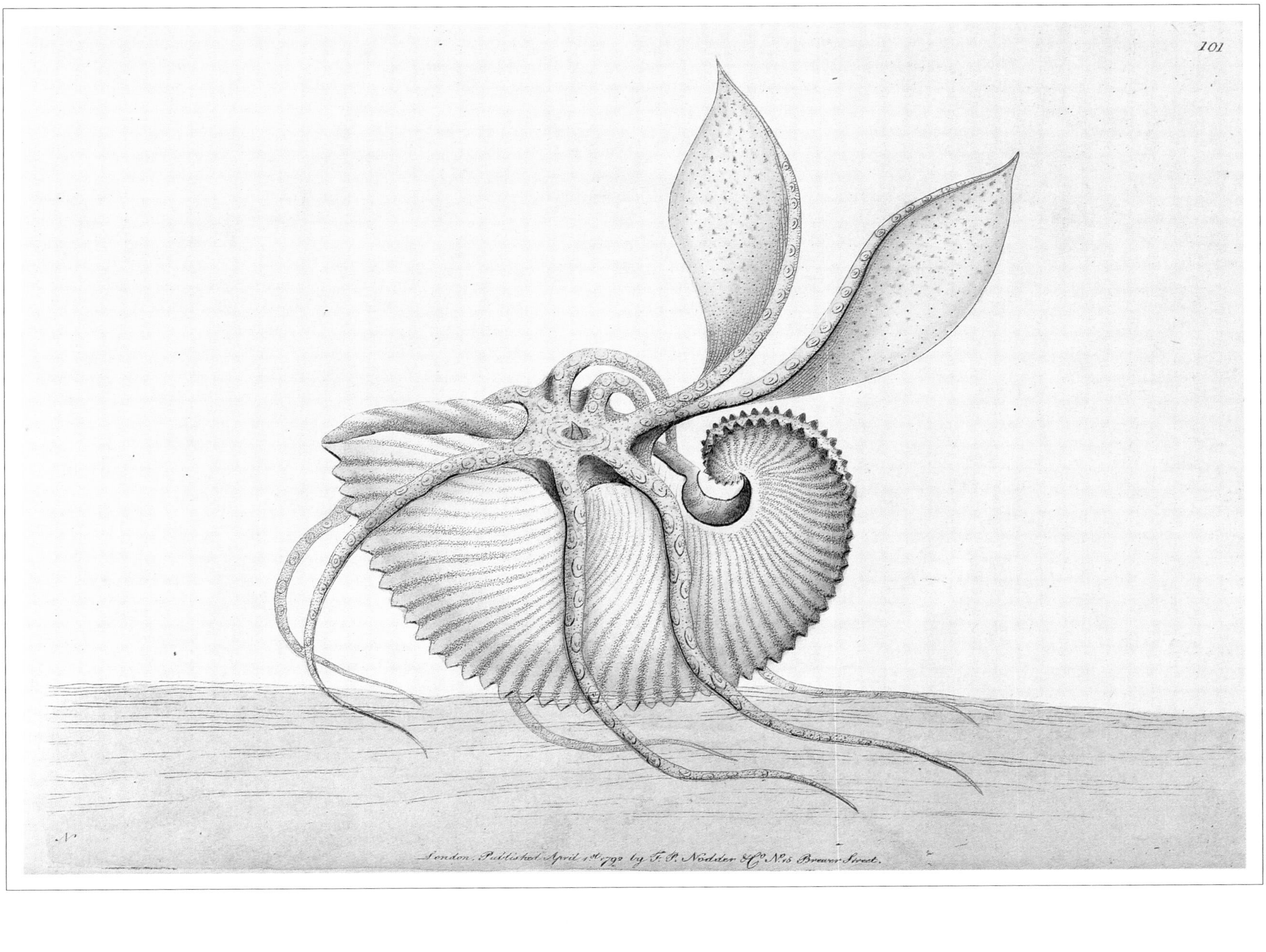
101
N
London, Published April 1st 1790 by F. P. Nodder & Co. No. 15 Brewer Street.

Mediterranean Scallops and Oysters (1795)

PETTINI E OSTRICHE (Scallops and Oysters). Hand-coloured copper engraving by N. Cesarano from original drawings by F. Morelli, pl. 28 from Vol 2. (1795) of G.S. Poli's *Testacea utriusque Siciliae eorumque Historia et Anatome &c*, 1791–5. Size of plate 17″ × 12″.

Giuseppe Saverio Poli chose well when he abandoned his medical practice to dedicate himself to natural science and took up residence in Naples, once the largest city in Italy and capital of a kingdom ruled by Bourbon French kings. Sicily was later added to form the Kingdom of the Two Sicilies. Poli's scientific interests were wide-ranging. He studied electricity and magnetism and had a particular fondness for thunderstorms. He wrote about earthquakes from first-hand experience, but his poetic work on astronomy "failed to arouse enthusiasm for either its artistic or scientific merits". Besides all this he had a famous collection of coins and medals, lectured on military history, and was Professor of Physics at the Royal Military Academy. No wonder, then, that Ferdinand IV, King of the Two Sicilies, summoned him to court to teach his son, the future Francis I.

This influential appointment was beneficial to Science in several ways. Poli not only provided the idea of founding the Naples botanical garden but also supplied rare plants for it; and at his insistence the Royal Library was opened up to scholars. Financial support from the court and the proximity of the sea enabled Poli to do extensive research in marine biology. For twelve years he studied Mediterranean molluscs with the help of the anatomist Michele Troja. The fruits of this labour were two sumptuous folio volumes, the *Testacea utriusque Siciliae* (Shells of the Two Sicilies), in which he outlined a new classification of molluscs based on his detailed anatomical descriptions. Niccolò Cesarano and Francesco Morelli were two of several artists whose beautiful engravings endow this work with a timeless value. This plate shows a selection of Mediterranean scallops (Pectinidae) of which no fewer than nine were first named and described here. Also shown are some file shells (Limidae) and oysters (Ostreidae), including, at bottom centre, a group of Poli's new species *Ostrea* (now *Neopycnodonte*) *cochlear*, attached to a stem of the black coral *Antipathes*.

Tab. XXVIII.

Morelli del.

Nic.º Cesarano Scul.

Noble Pen-shell (1795)

PINNA NOBILE, *Pinna nobilis* (now Noble Pen-shell). Hand-coloured copper engraving by Giovanni Ottaviani from original drawings by Giovanni Casanova, pl. 35 from Vol. 2 (1795) of G.S. Poli's *Testacea utriusque Siciliae eorumque Historia et Anatome &c*, 1791–5. Size of plate 18″ × 12¾″.

With access to the zoological wealth of the Bay of Naples and his royal patronage as tutor to the Prince, Poli was ideally placed to seek an answer to one of the most baffling problems of eighteenth-century zoology: the relationship between the soft-bodied mollusc and its hard shell. At that time the same kind of mollusc was thought to occur in different kinds of shells, so it was shells which were named and classified; molluscs were regarded merely as their inhabitants. Although not the first to recognize the importance of anatomy in understanding their proper affinities, Poli is justly recognized as one of the founders of the study of molluscs as distinct from the study of their shells only.

Wax models were made of Poli's careful dissections for teaching purposes and these finally dispelled the notion that all bivalves were much the same inside. Some of these models still survive in Strasbourg. Unfortunately his scientific legacy is not as unalloyed as we might wish. In his *Testacea utriusque Siciliae* Poli named many new genera based on anatomical differences, but he proposed a parallel set of names for their shells and also retained the older Linnaean names for the animal and shell together. This cumbersome system of naming molluscs caused Poli's otherwise excellent researches to be greatly undervalued by later generations.

One of the star attractions of the Bay of Naples for shell enthusiasts is the Noble Pen-shell, *Pinna nobilis*, a large specimen of which may reach three to four feet in length. Poli devoted five plates to this species, illustrating specimens which, although of more modest dimensions, well represent this attractive shell with its iridescent pearly interior. The silky, golden byssus, shown in the left-hand figure, anchors the *Pinna* to the sand. Poli informs us that the byssus was combed, made into thread and then woven into garments, such as socks or gloves, which were highly esteemed for their softness and brilliance. This craft was chiefly carried on at Taranto and in Sicily. He also says that a plug of byssus, without any added preparation, was believed to cure infections of the ear.

Tab. XXXV.

Jo. Casanova delin.   Jo. Ottaviani sculp.

Needle-shaped Shells (1802)

STROMBIFORMES, or needle-shaped shells (now various elongated but unrelated gastropods). Hand-coloured engraving by John Chapman from original figures of A. Seba, pl. 12 of "Conchology" from Vol. 5 (1802–3) of J. Wilkes's *Encyclopaedia Londinensis; or, an Universal Dictionary of Arts, Sciences, and Literature*, 1796–1829. Size of plate 9¼″ × 7¾″.

The *Systema Naturae* of Linnaeus became the foundation for several attempts to expand it still further and translate it into other languages. One of the more ambitious of these schemes was that of Ebenezer Sibly, who conceived the idea of a *Universal System of Natural History* which would include not only all the most recent discoveries but also figures reproduced from the best of the illustrated works. For the molluscs these would include the works of Albertus Seba and Georg Wolfgang Knorr. Sibly died in 1800 after only three volumes had appeared, but the work was taken up by John Wilkes, who at that time was also involved in the publication of the *Encyclopaedia Londinensis*. Both ventures were long lived, the *Universal System of Natural History* spanning the sixteen years from 1794 to 1810, the *Encyclopaedia Londinensis* the thirty-five years from 1796 to 1829.

Wilkes adopted Sibly's idea of reviving the best of the earlier illustrations in his *Encyclopaedia*. Of the sixteen plates accompanying the article on "Conchology", four are taken from Knorr and twelve, including the one reproduced here, from Seba. This plate is actually a rehash of Plate 56 from the third volume of Seba's *Thesaurus*. As that volume was published in 1758, the fantastic colours and the arrangement of the shells in artistic patterns must have seemed as bizarre in 1802, when this plate was published, as they do today. The text of the article was probably written by Edward Donovan, but the classification he used, in which he grouped together all long and slender shells as "Strombiformes", was adapted from one proposed by E.M. da Costa in 1776. With no anatomical knowledge of molluscs himself, Donovan could only produce a classification of desperation for the varied assemblage of shells shown on this plate.

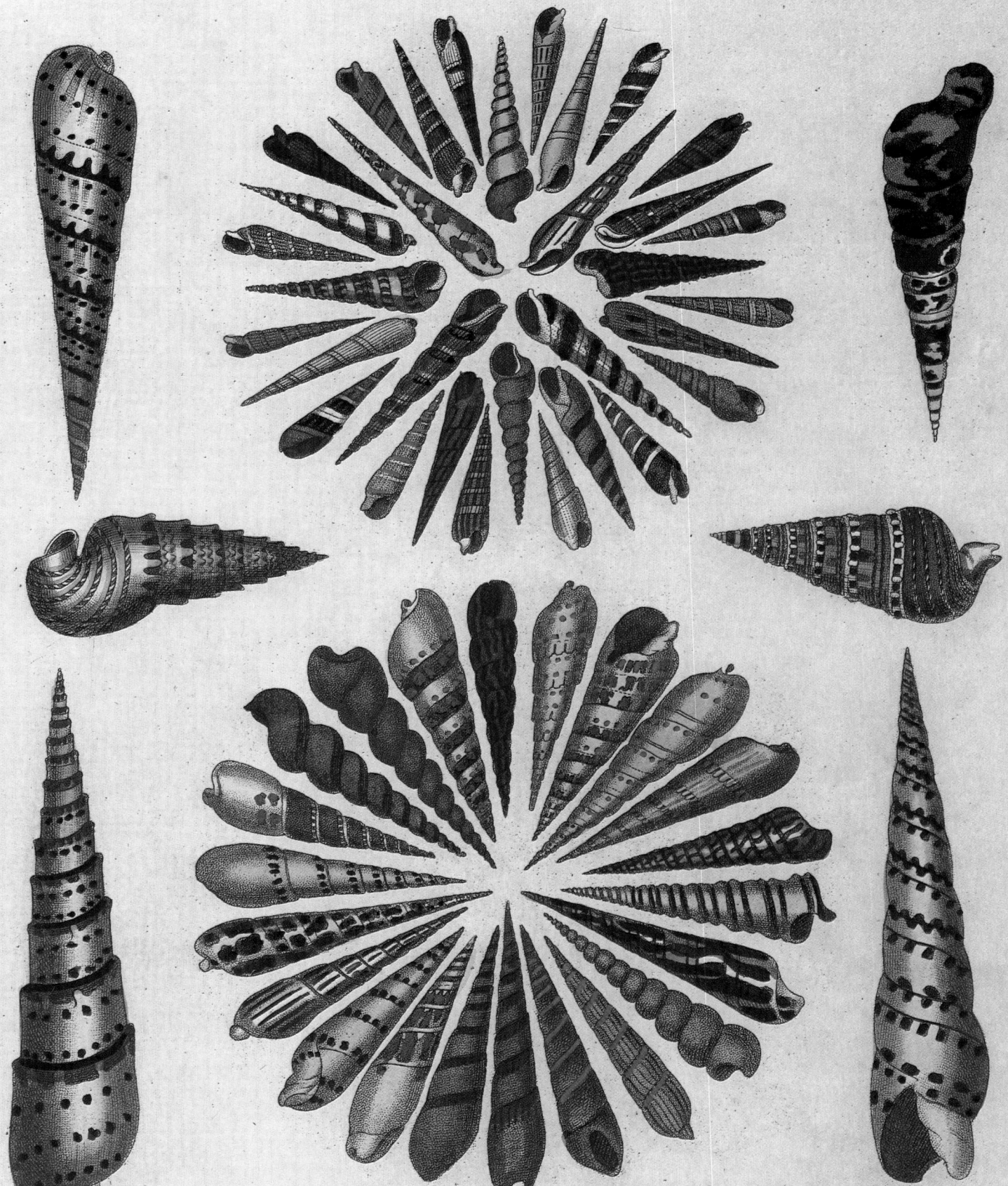

Albertus Seba del.

J. Chapman sc.

Strombiformes, or Needle-shaped Shells.

London Published as the Act directs Nov.r 6. 1802 by J. Wilkes.

Elongate Spider-conch and Others (1811)

STROMBUS DIGITATUS (now Elongate Spider-conch, *Lambis digitata*) (top) and others. Hand-coloured aquatint, pl. 13 from G. Perry's *Conchology, or the Natural History of Shells &c*, 1811. Size of plate 12¾″ × 9″.

The sixty-one plates of George Perry's *Conchology* are like no others in the literature of natural history, the bold lines and garish colouring often giving many of the figures a surreal quality. Perry's new generic names were imaginative and idiosyncratic too; but surrealism and idiosyncrasy were unwelcome in natural history circles in the early years of the nineteenth century, and his book was criticized harshly by members of the scientific establishment. He was even accused of dreaming of extraordinary shells and committing them to paper on waking! Perry's *Conchology* has been dealt with more kindly in our own day, and many of his new names of genera and species are now accepted.

Among the new species he introduced in the book was what is now known as the Elongate Spider-conch, *Lambis digitata*. One of the most striking members of a tropical group, it was seldom seen in collections before the twentieth century and is uncommon even now. It is patchily distributed from Samoa in the Pacific westwards to East Africa. Even Perry's harshest critics would have had to admit that this robust, six-inch-long shell was well delineated in his notorious *Conchology*.

Tent Olive and Others (1811)

Oliva leveriana (now Tent Olive, *Oliva porphyria*) (centre) and others. Hand-coloured aquatint, pl. 41 from G. Perry's *Conchology, or the Natural History of Shells &c*, 1811. Size of plate 12½" × 9".

Perry did not need to be a man of science to gain access to well-stocked shell cabinets. These were usually the property of the wealthy, who could indulge their passion for collecting novel, rare and curious objects. Their knowledge of science was often minimal, but their vanity could be tickled by the prospect of seeing their names and their treasures immortalized in print. So we find his *Conchology* liberally peppered with the names of the principal collectors of his day, noblemen and personages less exalted – but equally acquisitive and vain.

"Mr. Jennings of Chelsea" belonged to the latter category. Henry Constantine Jennings was a strange character who spent so much money on rare and unusual objects, natural and artificial, that he was imprisoned twice for insolvency. His shell collection was outstanding in its day and provided Perry with several unique items, including the odd-looking shell at the bottom right of this plate. Dubbed *Oliva subviridis* by him, nothing approaching it in appearance has ever been found outside this plate, like some other "species" portrayed in the *Conchology*. The central figure represents a shell he called *Oliva leveriana*, which was "formerly in the Museum of the late Sir Ashton Lever, in honour of whose zeal for the promotion of natural history and the sciences, I have taken this opportunity of naming it". His belated tribute – Sir Ashton had died twenty-three years previously – was a waste of time because this flashy species, popularly known as the Tent Olive and a familiar sight in shallow water from Panama to the Gulf of California, had been described by Linnaeus many years earlier, as *Oliva porphyria*.

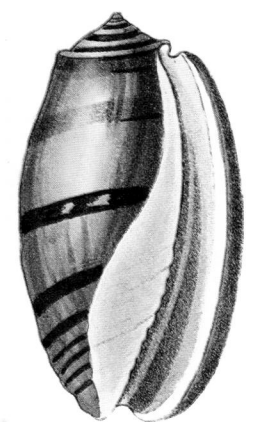

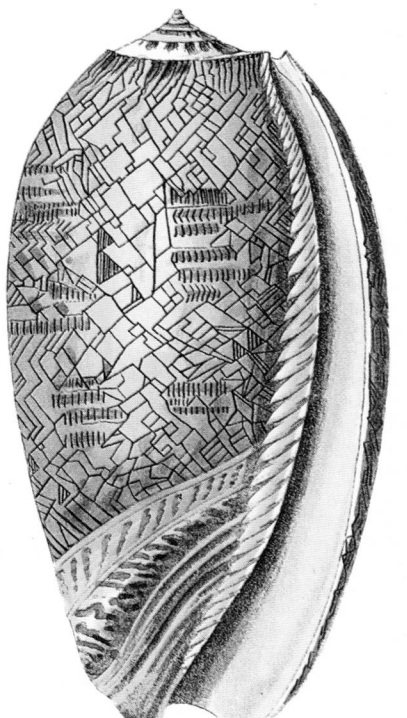

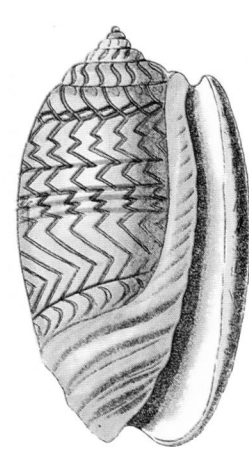

London Pub. by W. Miller, 1813.

Tun Shells and Others (1813)

Tun Shells (Tonnidae), and others. Hand-coloured aquatint, probably engraved by Warner from original drawings by William Newton, unnumbered plate from B. Rolfe's *Testaceologia Universalis; or a General System of Conchology &c*, 1813. Size of plate 11″ × 8¾″.

"In order to put the English reader in possession of a complete System of Conchology, comprehending and illustrating the whole of the Science, we have been induced to undertake the present work, in compliance with the advice and under the patronage of the most celebrated Naturalists of this country." So said Benjamin Rolfe in the Preface to his *Testaceologia Universalis*, little suspecting that his grand scheme would survive to posterity in one unique copy comprising only three leaves of text and five aquatinted plates. Rolfe was elected a Fellow of the Linnean Society of London in 1811, when he was living at Bermondsey in London. Apart from that we know almost nothing about him and can only guess that his ambitious publication fizzled out for lack of support.

This plate shows that the illustrations were good for the period, and they share with those in Perry's *Conchology* the distinction of being the only representations of shells to be reproduced by the expensive aquatint process. Had Rolfe continued publication in this manner he would have been put to a very considerable expense because, as he says later in his Preface, it was his intention to give "a correct figure of every species and remarkable variety of marine, fresh-water, and terrestrial shell hitherto discovered, the very minute ones excepted, accompanied with the scientific description and natural history of all the animal inhabitants that can possibly be procured, with their names, habitations, manners, oeconomy, and appearance; exhibiting, at one view, a systematic and scientific arrangement of class, order, genus, species, and variety, in a clear, simple, compendious, and accurate manner". Rolfe may have been over-confident and naïve; undoubtedly he was over-optimistic and verbose.

Giant Baler (1821)

SHORT-CROWNED MELON, *Voluta diadema* (now Giant Baler, *Melo amphora*). Hand-coloured lithograph, pl. [1] from the first edition of W. Swainson's *Exotic Conchology &c*, 1821–2. Size of plate 11½" × 9".

William Swainson said that his drawing had been made "from a young but uncommonly beautiful shell in the Bligh collection". As its common name suggests, it would have grown much larger, specimens up to twenty inches long having been reported. A well-known species in Australian waters, this immature shell may have been obtained while he was governor of New South Wales by William Bligh, of *Bounty* fame, to grace the collection amassed by his wife Elizabeth. Swainson illustrated several of Elizabeth Bligh's shells in his *Exotic Conchology*. He also helped compile and illustrate the catalogue of her fine collection which was sold at auction in 1822.

The *Exotic Conchology* is one of the most exquisitely illustrated books about shells ever published, Swainson copying his original drawings onto the lithographic stones himself. He intended his book to be a luxury production but, for various reasons, he abandoned it unfinished. Perfect copies of the first edition and the expanded second edition of 1834–5 are rare and print dealers find a ready sale for individual plates culled from the few copies which come onto the market.

Voluta diadema. Lam.

Mus: Dom:ᵃ Bligh.

Chorus Mussel (1821)

MOULE EN SABOT, *Mytilus ungulatus* (now Chorus Mussel, *Choromytilus chorus*). Hand-coloured etching by Jean Louis Denis Coutant from original drawings by Huet, pl. 49 of A. Valenciennes's "Coquilles marines bivalves de l'Amérique Équinoxiale" from Part 2, Zoology (1812–33), of F.H.A. von Humboldt and A.J.A. Bonpland's *Voyage aux Régions Équinoxiales du Nouveau Continent, fait en 1799–1804 &c*, 1805–37. Size of plate 12½″ × 9¾″.

This illustration is tucked away in one of the thirty massive volumes describing the results of Baron Alexander von Humboldt's scientific explorations in the Americas. Between 1799 and 1803, accompanied by the French botanist Aimé Bonpland, he investigated many aspects of South American natural history, including the coastal fauna and flora. The reports on the fishes and the molluscs they collected were entrusted to Achille Valenciennes, who was overjoyed to have his name printed alongside Humboldt's. One of the few marine molluscs the two explorers brought back to Europe, the Chorus Mussel was described by Valenciennes as a large and beautiful shell from the coasts of Peru and Chile "remarkable for its triangular form which approaches that of a cow's hoof". Attaining a length of about six inches, it is one of the largest mussels in the sea.

Its popular name is derived from its scientific name and implies that it is grape-coloured. As its outer surface is normally covered by a thick, dull skin, the aptness of that name is not immediately apparent, although it could denote the shell's internal colouring. But when the outer surface is rubbed down and polished it becomes a beautiful lustrous purple, in which condition it used to be highly prized by shell collectors and was often used in jewellery. As its edges may also be filed to a razor-sharpness, early natives along the west coast of South America as far south as the Straits of Magellan discovered that the Chorus Mussel made a very useful tool.

Pl. XLIX

1. a.

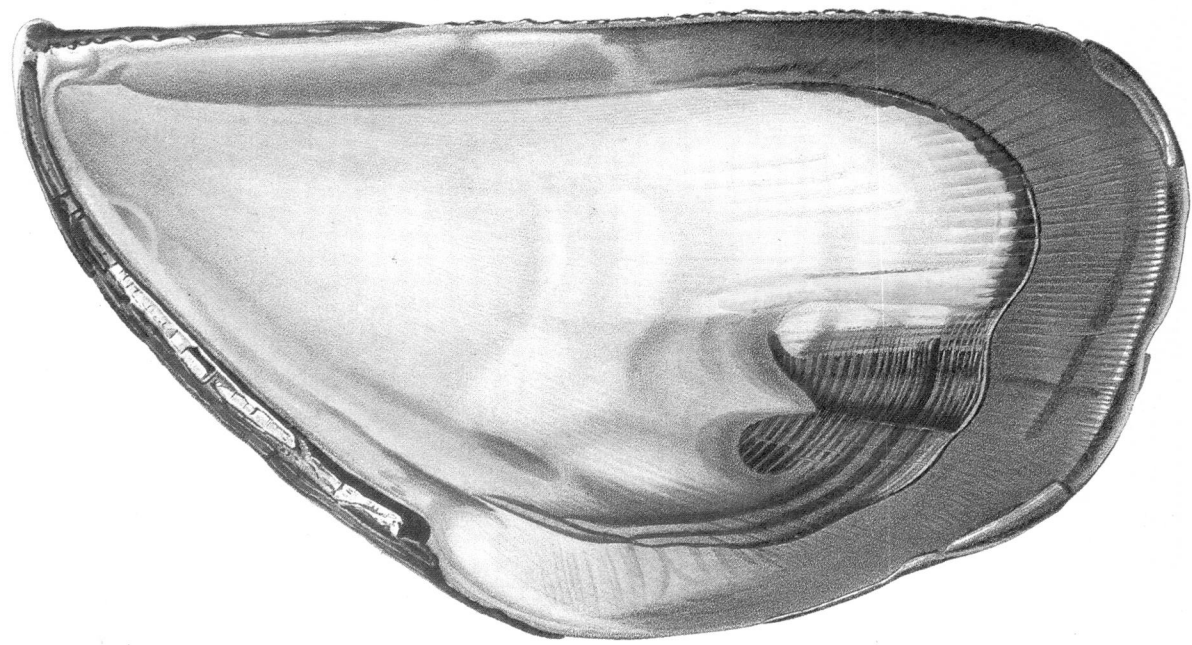

1. b.

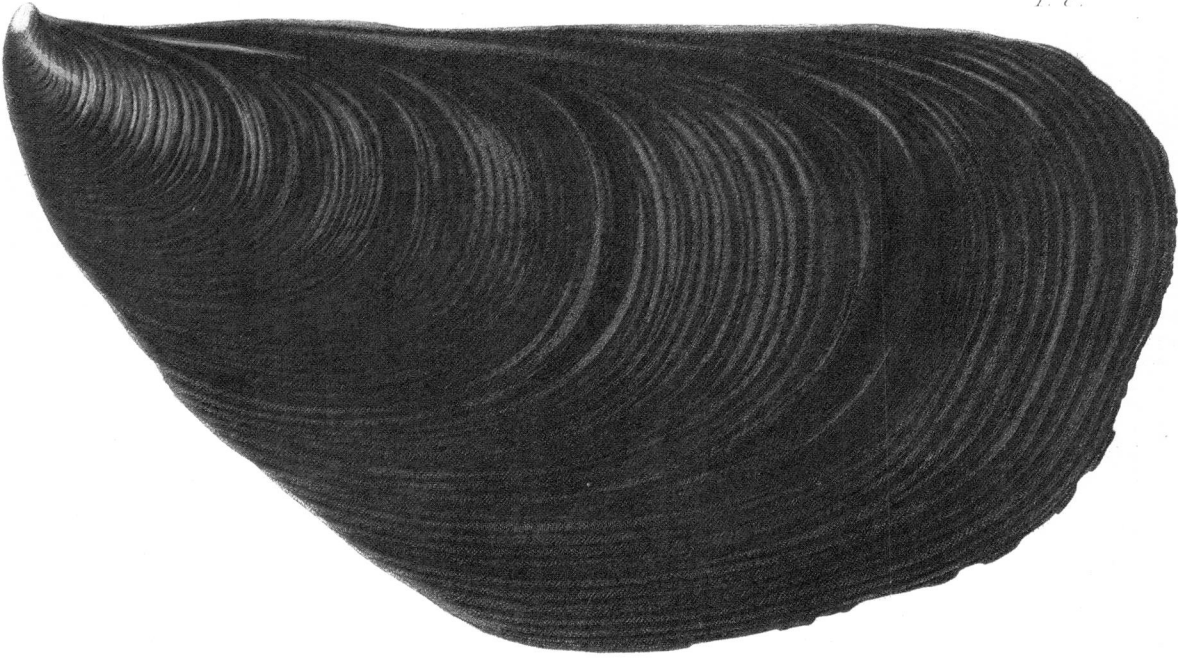

1. c.

Dessiné par Bari d'après les esquisses de M.ʳ de Humboldt.

Gravé par Coutant.

De l'Imprimerie de Langlois.

True Achatina (1823)

COCHLITOME AGATHINE, *Helix achatina* (now True Achatina, *Achatina achatina*). Hand-coloured engraving by Jean Louis Denis Coutant from original drawings by Huet, pl. 131 from Part 20 (1823) of J.B.L. d'Audebard, Baron de Férussac's *Histoire Naturelle Générale et Particulière des Mollusques Terrestres et Fluviatiles*, 1819–32. Size of plate 12¼″ × 9″.

This plate, taken from the first large-scale treatise on land shells, by Jean Baptiste Louis d'Audebard, Baron de Férussac, illustrates the True Achatina, the world's largest land snail. By contrast with most of the plates in this selection, the shells are displayed with their apertures uppermost – a convention preferred by most French conchologists up to the first half of the twentieth century. Férussac's book, still noteworthy for the accuracy and beauty of its many folio plates, was costly and time-consuming to produce and is still valued highly by scientists and antiquarian-book lovers alike. Most of the book appeared posthumously and its publication was superintended by Baron de Férussac's son André Étienne.

The exclusively vegetarian True Achatina comes from northern parts of West Africa, where it lives in dense forests. Occasionally reaching a length of eight inches, the shell contains an animal of equally formidable size. Natives from Liberia to Nigeria supplement their diet with the meat this huge snail provides; and in Ghana this and other related species have been important sources of protein for many years. According to an English translation of a treatise on farming by the Roman writer Varro, certain snails "come from Africa, called *Solitannae*, which are so big that 80 *quadrantes* can be put into their shells". The translator interprets this to mean that one of these shells could contain three gallons – an impossibility for any known land shell – but there is an alternative, more acceptable interpretation of Varro's statement. The *quadrans* was a thin copper coin about three-quarters of an inch (or two centimetres) in diameter. A shell of the True Achatina, or one of its relatives, could certainly hold about eighty of these.

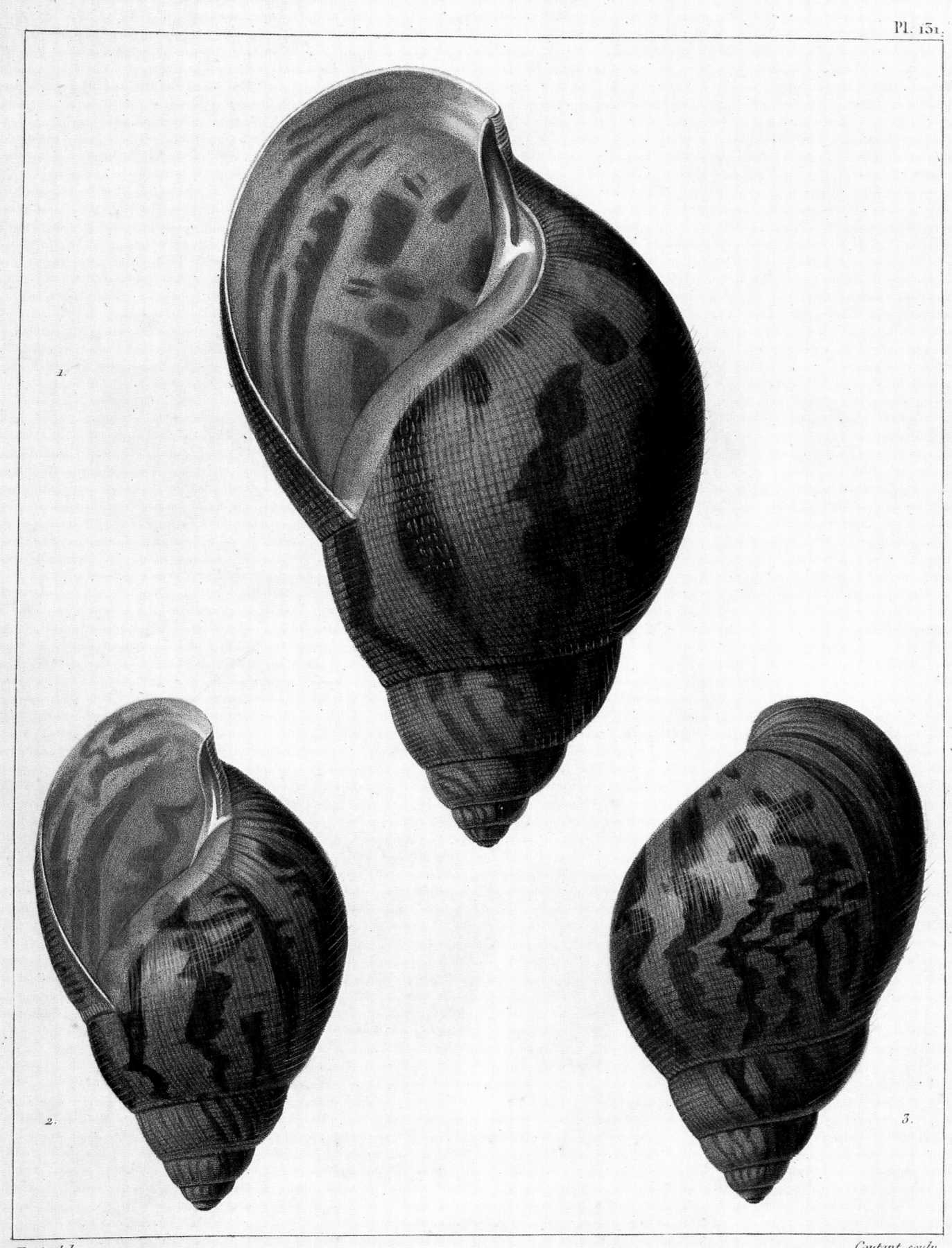

Pl. 131.

Huet del.

Coutant sculp.

LIMAÇONS, genre *HÉLICE* (*S. G. Cochlitome, achatinæ.*)

De l'Imprimerie de Langlois.

Glory-of-the-Sea Cone (1825)

GLORY-OF-THE-SEA CONE, *Conus gloriamaris* (two larger figures). Hand-coloured engraving by G.B. Sowerby (1st), unnumbered plate from his *Catalogue of the Shells contained in the Collection of the Late Earl of Tankerville*, 1825. Size of plate 8″ × 5¼″.

In 1825 George Brettingham Sowerby, the first of three members of an artistic family to bear that name, was commissioned to sell the valuable and extensive shell collection of the fourth Earl of Tankerville. To help promote the sale, he published a partly illustrated catalogue of its contents, usually called *The Tankerville Catalogue*. The illustrations were of high quality and provided a foretaste of the enormous output of conchological illustrations which were to emanate from the Sowerby family establishment over the coming years.

The most celebrated shell in the Tankerville collection was a large and fine example of the Glory-of-the-Sea Cone, the most coveted shell of the nineteenth century. Only three or four specimens were known at that time, no one knew where it lived, and this was the first specimen to be put up for public sale in Britain. Of course this five-inch-long rarity had to be made the subject of one of the few plates associated with the catalogue and, as may be seen, the engraving of it was done with great attention to detail, the myriad fine lines covering it being faithfully copied. The shell was sold to William J. Broderip, whose valuable collection is now in the Natural History Museum in London. This example of the once legendary Glory-of-the-Sea Cone may still be seen there, a little faded but otherwise perfect. Not until the 1950s was it definitely established that the headquarters of the species is the Philippines. Nowadays, good specimens may be purchased from dealers, who have no difficulty maintaining a stock of them. Sowerby's excellent picture of it reminds us of a time when it was the despair of every collector who wanted to own one.

1. 2. *Conus Gloria Maris.*
3. 4. .... *vespertinus.*

Shells illustrating Lamarck's Genera (1827)

SHELLS illustrating Lamarck's Genera. Hand-coloured lithograph by E.A. Crouch, pl. 19 from his *Illustrated Introduction to Lamarck's Conchology*, 1827. Size of plate 12½" × 10".

For more than fifty years conchology was studied within the framework proposed by Linnaeus in his *Systema Naturae* of 1758 in which all the molluscs then known were arranged in a few genera. It was a simple arrangement, hallowed by long usage, but it did not satisfy Jean Baptiste Pierre Antoine de Monet, Chevalier de Lamarck. At the end of the eighteenth century, when in his fifties, he began publishing his own ideas about the arrangement of molluscs and eventually proposed many new genera to accommodate them. Unfortunately his publications were unillustrated and it was difficult, especially for Britons isolated from the Continent by Napoleon's antics, to visualize his new genera, correspondingly difficult to arrange a shell collection according to them. To overcome these difficulties, one or two books describing and illustrating the Lamarckian system of conchology were published. The most attractively illustrated of them was Edmund A. Crouch's *Illustrated Introduction to Lamarck's Conchology*.

By illustrating one or more of the species included in each genus of Lamarck's arrangement, as published in his *Histoire Naturelle des Animaux sans Vertèbres*, 1815–22, Crouch provided a useful service for shell collectors. The central figure on this plate, for instance, represents the Crenulate Auger, *Terebra crenulata*, a species placed by Linnaeus in the genus *Buccinum* and by Lamarck in his new genus *Terebra*. Crouch's figure showed collectors what *Terebra* shells looked like and enabled them to recognize similar shells in their own collections. The high quality of his lithographs must have helped identification. Although a few copies of Crouch's book are dated 1826 on the title page, it seems that 1827 was the true date of publication.

Fig.1.

Pl. 19.

Smooth Callista and Others (1827)

CYTHERIA CHIONE (now Smooth Callista, *Callista chione*) (top centre) and others. Hand-coloured engraving by W.H. Lizars from original drawings by Captain T. Brown, pl. 19 from Part 6 of the first edition of Brown's *Illustrations of the Conchology of Great Britain and Ireland*, 1827. Size of plate 10¾″ × 9″.

Thomas Brown, born in Perth and educated in Edinburgh, enlisted in the Forfar and Kincardineshire militia at the age of twenty. From that time onwards he was universally known as Captain Thomas Brown. Later, having lost all his money when his flax mill burned down uninsured, and with a wife and daughter to support, Brown resolved to make his living as a scientific author. He returned to Edinburgh, where he wrote many works on natural history, especially on conchology. He drew and coloured many of his own illustrations, with William Home Lizars and others making the engravings. Brown reused illustrations, and even large sections of text, in several different works, and there are other tell-tale signs of the pressure he had to work under. The arrangement of the plates and portions of the text were often revised even as publication was in progress.

For some of his books it is difficult to find two copies exactly alike. The first edition of Brown's *Illustrations of the Conchology of Great Britain and Ireland* is one such example. In some copies the plate numbers have been altered in ink or have new numbers pasted over them, and some have Arabic and others Roman numerals (for instance Plate XIX, shown here, was originally Plate XXXVI). Furthermore the figures, drawn from the largest and best specimens Brown could obtain, are sometimes spoiled by hurried colouring. Brown presumably had a little more leisure after he became Curator of the Manchester Natural History Society's Museum in 1838.

Apart from the large, black Iceland Cyprina, *Arctica islandica* (bottom centre), the plate depicts various British venus shells and carpet shells. Many of these are eaten in continental Europe, especially the Smooth Callista (top centre) which in Britain occurs only in the south and west of the country in clean sand.

PLATE XIX.

Drawn by Capt.Brown.

Engraved by W.H.Lizars Edinburgh.

Limpet-like Shells (1828)

PATELLA, Limpet (actually a miscellaneous assortment of shells, belonging to several families, each shell having a limpet-like shape). Hand-coloured engraving by W. Wood (junior), pl. 37 from the third edition of W. Wood (senior's) *Index Testaceologicus; or a Catalogue of Shells, British and Foreign &c*, 1828. Size of plate 6¾″ × 4″.

Until the second half the nineteenth century, natural history books were expensive, especially when illustrated with plates coloured by hand. William Wood, a surgeon-turned-bookseller, was aware that money could be made from a low-priced book which brought together many coloured illustrations of shells. In the Preface to his *Index Testaceologicus* he says he had endeavoured to provide, as a substitute for large and expensive publications, "a work which will incorporate in one volume figures of all the known shells, reduced indeed to a small size, but with a degree of accuracy that it is hoped, will not only enable the conchologist to fix upon any particular species he may wish to define, but also to arrange his collection by inspection, without the trouble of consulting other publications on the subject". His son provided engravings of most of the 2,300 shells illustrated, many of them copied from the expensive books the *Index* was intended to supplant, each one requiring hand colouring – a daunting task for a single copy of the book, let alone an entire edition – and a complicated series of symbols showed the actual sizes of the shells. The book was so successful that a fourth edition, revised extensively by Sylvanus Hanley, was published in 1856.

The classification of shells in the *Index* reflects the state of conchological knowledge in Wood's day. The shells illustrated here, for instance, were all supposed to be members of the Linnaean genus *Patella*, the scientific name of the limpets found commonly on European and other shores, but although a few of those illustrated are true limpets, the others are quite unrelated.

Pl 37

Butterfly Cone (1831)

NICOL'S CONE, *Conus nicolii* (now Butterfly Cone, *Conus pulcher*). Hand-coloured engraving by William Home Lizars, pl. 36 from Part 10 (1831) of J. Wilson's *Illustrations of Zoology*, 1827–31. Size of plate 16″ × 12″.

James Wilson's illustration of the shell he called Nicol's Cone is unlike any other in this selection. By placing the shell on a rocky and sandy beach with a tree-lined shore as a backdrop – an imaginative if improbable setting for a shell normally confined to shallow water offshore – the artist conveys the impression that this subject was picked up on such a beach. Perhaps it was, but Wilson's text does not enlighten us. "This being the only individual of the species which I have had an opportunity of inspecting," he says, "I am unable to describe its appearance in the various stages of its growth. It has the aspect, however, of a very old individual, and is probably more highly coloured in the younger states. Nothing is known as to the native country of this singular specimen, hitherto unrivalled as to magnitude." With a length of eight and a half inches it is unquestionably a very large example of the West African species now known as the Butterfly Cone, usually fully grown at about four inches.

Wilson, certain the shell represented a previously undescribed species, seized the opportunity to honour the name of the man whose shell collection it graced. "I have named it in honour of its owner Mr William Nicol of Edinburgh," he said, "whose extensive collection of shells has ever been open to the inspection of the curious, and whose scientific knowledge in conchology, as well as in other departments of natural history, is worthy of a tribute, which I should not have thought of paying to the mere possessor of a unique specimen." William Nicol is still remembered as the inventor of a prism which bears his name, but his scientific attainments in crystallography and palaeontology have been almost entirely forgotten. This shell, more impressive by its size than its beauty, has finally come to rest, with the remainder of Nicol's shell collection, in the National Museums of Scotland in Edinburgh.

PLATE XXXVI.

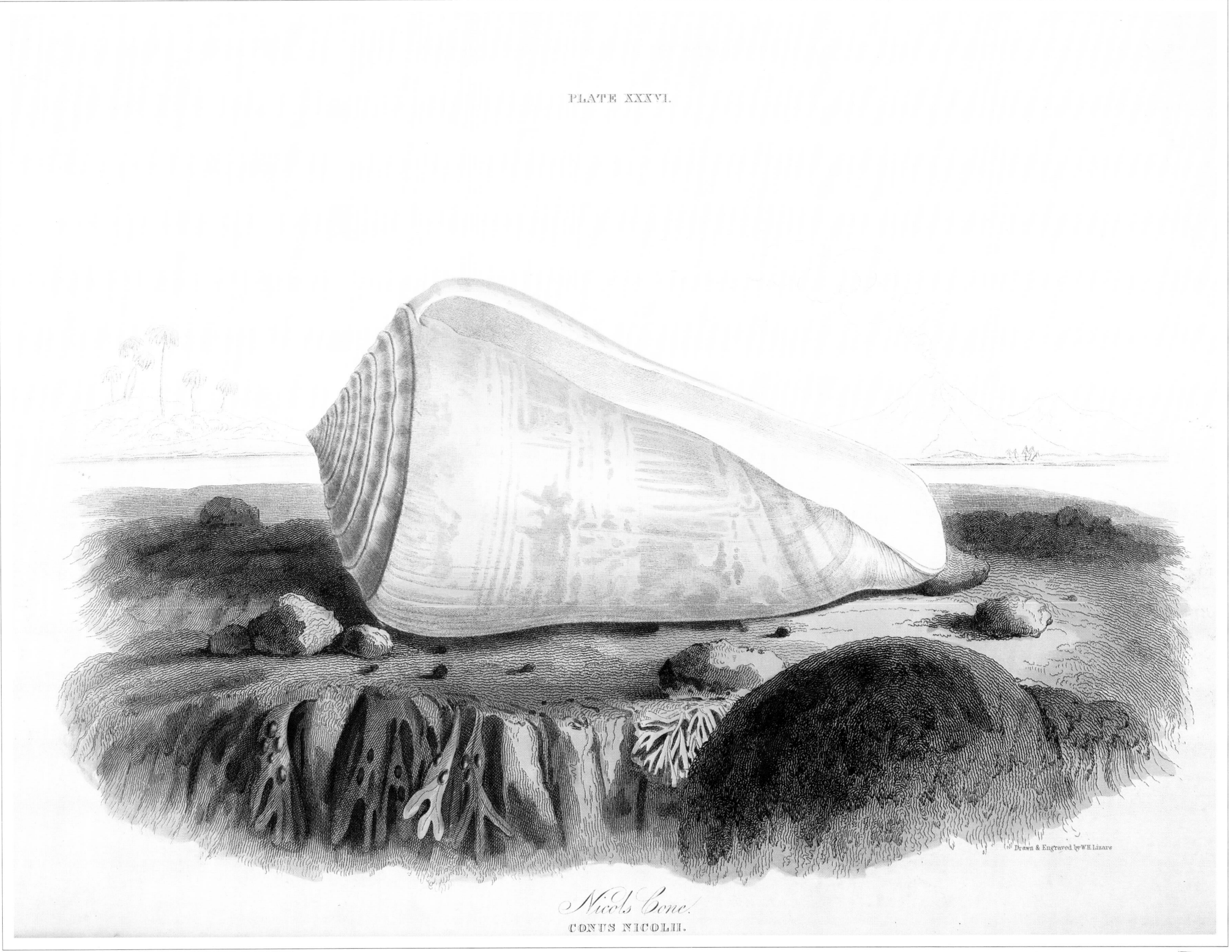

Nicols Cone.

CONUS NICOLII.

Umbrella Squid (c. 1835)

CRANCHIA BONELLIANA (now Umbrella Squid, *Histioteuthis bonnellii*). Hand-coloured lithograph by A. Chazal, pl. 2 of *Cranchia* from A.É. d'Audebard, Baron de Férussac, and A.D. d'Orbigny's, *Monographie des Céphalopodes Cryptodibranches*, 1834–5. Size of plate 10″ × 7½″.

This dramatic illustration of the two-foot-long Umbrella Squid was drawn by Antoine Chazal, Professor of Iconography at the Jardin des Plantes in Paris. It shows the right side of an adult female from underneath and comes from a pioneering work on squids and other cephalopods. The elongated light organs on the tips of the arms and the ring of seventeen light organs surrounding the right eye are clearly visible. It must have been difficult for Chazal to visualize the appearance of this curious animal, which lives at depths from 250 to 6 500 feet in the northern Atlantic and Mediterranean, because it was probably brought to him preserved in a jar, possibly accompanied by brief notes and a sketch or two.

Largest of the thirteen species of *Histioteuthis*, the Umbrella Squid normally swims at an angle of thirty to forty-five degrees, with the tail held higher than the large head, but it can also hover in the head-down position, using the two small, oval tail-fins. The arms are connected by a wide, maroon-coloured inner web (the umbrella), but the two long tentacles are free. The eyes are asymmetrical, the right one (shown here) being much smaller than the left. The larger eye looks upward and is adapted for vision in the upper layers of the sea where the sunlight penetrates dimly; the smaller one looks downward and forward and is sensitive to bioluminescence in the ocean depths. The squid's entire underside is dotted with many light organs which produce a very successful camouflage by counter-illumination. The brightness and colour of the luminescence can be closely matched to that of the dim light from above, making the animal effectively disappear. Without the lights the squid, seen from below, would be silhouetted against the sky. This ingenious camouflage is of limited use, however, as most of its predators do not hunt by sight.

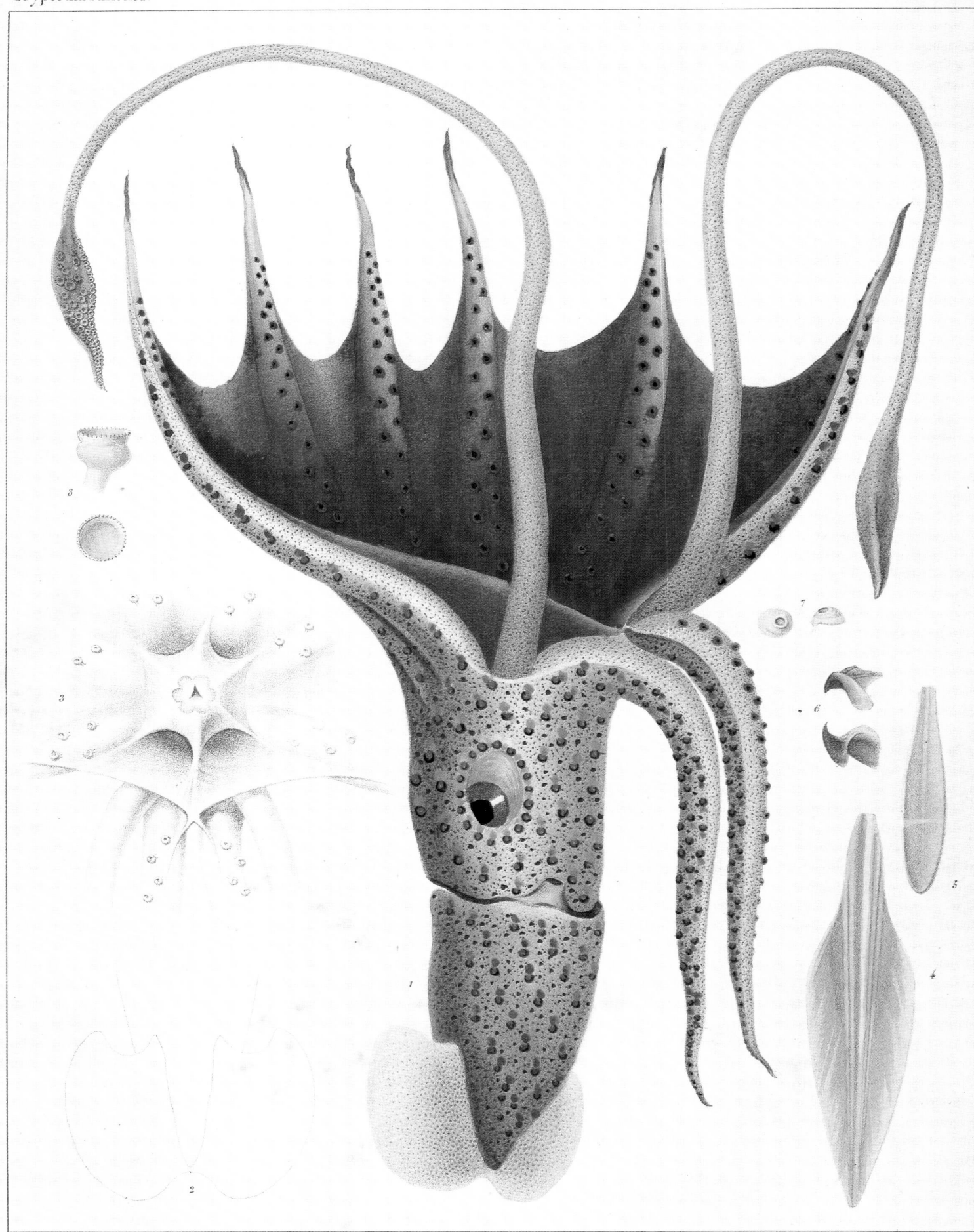

G. Chazal pinx.   A. Chazal ad Lapid del.

Cranchia Bonelliana, Férussac.

Blanket Octopus (c. 1839)

OCTOPUS VIOLACEUS (now Blanket Octopus, *Tremoctopus violaceus*). Hand-coloured lithograph by A. Benard from a drawing by Émile Théophile Blanchard (a copy of an original figure by S. delle Chiaje), pl. 20 of *Octopus* from A.É. d'Audebard, Baron de Férussac, and A.D. d'Orbigny's *Histoire Naturelle Générale et Particulière des Céphalopodes Acétabulifères*, 1834–48. Size of plate 11¼″ × 8½″.

The work from which this plate is taken is a continuation of the one detailed on the previous page. Both form part of a larger work projected by Férussac's father, J.B. d'Audebard, Baron de Férussac, the *Histoire Naturelle des Mollusques*, which was never completed. Shown here is an adult female of the Blanket Octopus viewed from above. One of the two known species of *Tremoctopus* (a newspaper may be read through the transparent body of the other one), it frequents warm and tropical waters around the globe, rising to the surface at night. Although not abundant, it may sometimes appear in great numbers; tens of thousands were reported from the Northern Adriatic in 1936.

Females are two to three feet in length, dwarfing the one-inch-long males. The illustration shows the characteristic paired water pores on the upper side of the head; a second pair is on the underside. Adult females are dark blue-purple to wine red above, with the underside bright silvery gold; males and juveniles are bright with small dark points. In the females the first two pairs of arms are connected by a wide fringing web bearing large iridescent clusters of green, eye-like spots. In young females each arm of the first pair is very long. If attacked, a small piece of one of these long arms, comprising a sucker and one, two or three coloured spots, is detached and expands suddenly to the size of a pocket handkerchief, the spots blazing as it does so. This performance distracts and probably frightens the attacker, allowing the octopus to escape. So, although these long arms of the female continue to grow, their ends are always broken off and they are invariably shorter than the second pair of arms. Males and young females use suckers on their first pair of arms to carry small pieces of stinging tentacles taken from the Portuguese Man-of-war, *Physalia*, to provide an additional defence.

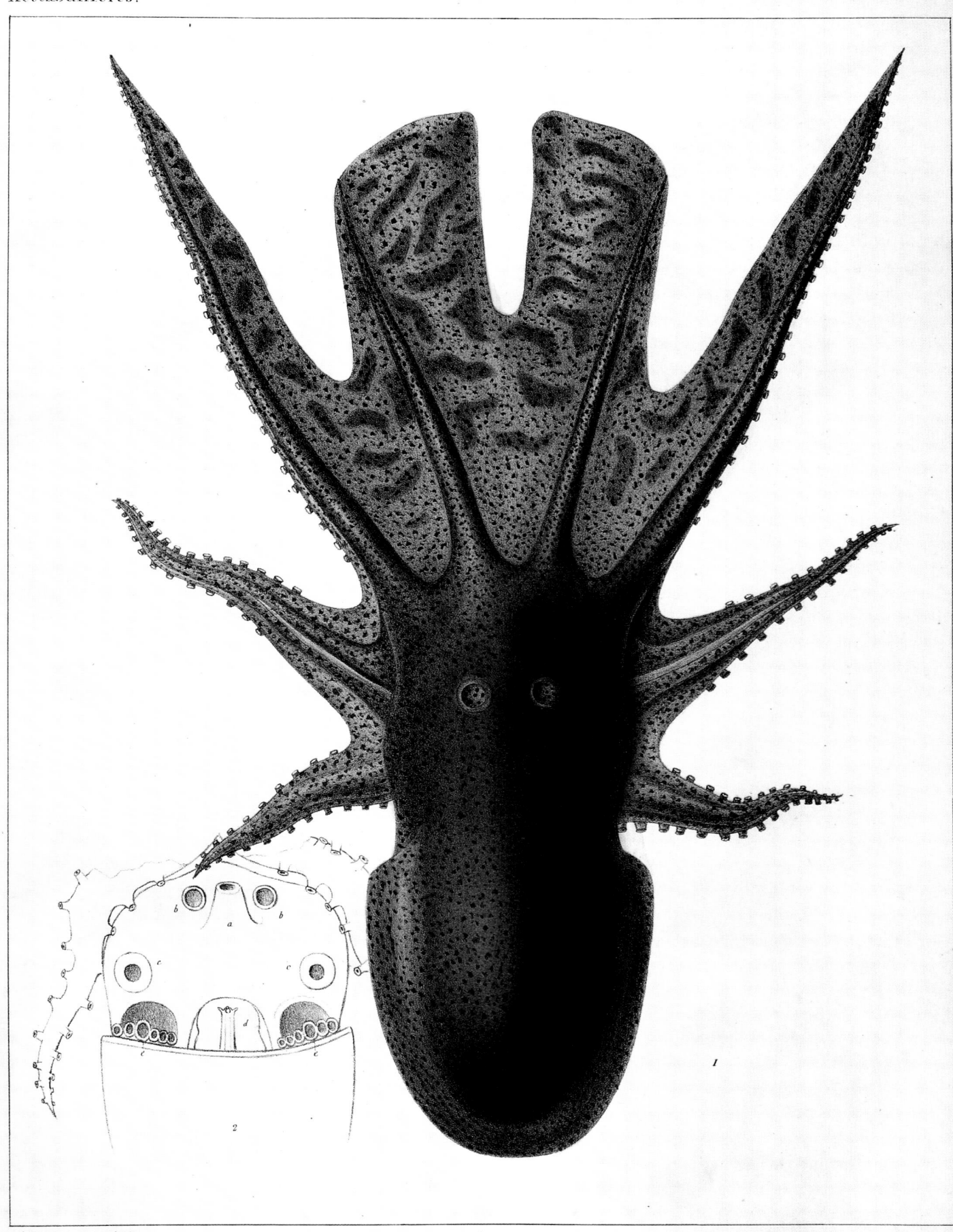

E. Blanchard. ad. Lapid. delin.

Lith. de Benard.

O. Violaceus. Delle Chiaje.

Cabbage Murex and Others (1839)

Murex brassica (now Cabbage Murex, *Phyllonotus brassica*) (centre) and others. Hand-coloured engraving by G.B. Sowerby (1st), pl. 33 of J.E. Gray's "Molluscous Animals and their Shells" (1839) from *The Zoology of Captain Beechey's Voyage . . . in H.M.S. Blossom . . . in the years 1825–28,* 1839. Size of plate 11″ × 8½″.

From 1825 to 1828 Captain Frederick William Beechey explored parts of the Pacific and the Behring Straits in command of the *Blossom*. He was instructed to bring back to London collections of animals and plants from the places visited and to make notes upon them. John Edward Gray, of the British Museum, was one of the specialists entrusted with the materials collected and he was supposed to write the report on Molluscous Animals and their Shells. Pressure of work delayed completion of the report and George Brettingham Sowerby (1st) was called in to put the finishing touches to it. The text was undistinguished but the plates, of which this is one of the most arresting, maintained the high standards associated with the name of Sowerby.

Dominating the plate is an exquisite engraving of the Cabbage Murex, described by the great French zoologist Lamarck as *Murex brassica*, one of the most striking shells of the west coast of Central and South America. During a visit to Paris, Gray was able to confirm the identification of the specimen illustrated. "I have compared this shell with Lamarck's own specimen, in the collection of the Prince Masséna", he says, "and it agrees with the one here figured in every particular; that it is the shell he described is proved by its having the name written on it by Lamarck himself." Even today specialists confirm the identity of certain species by examining specimens in the Lamarck collection, now one of the treasures housed in the Natural History Museum in Geneva.

Plate XXXIII

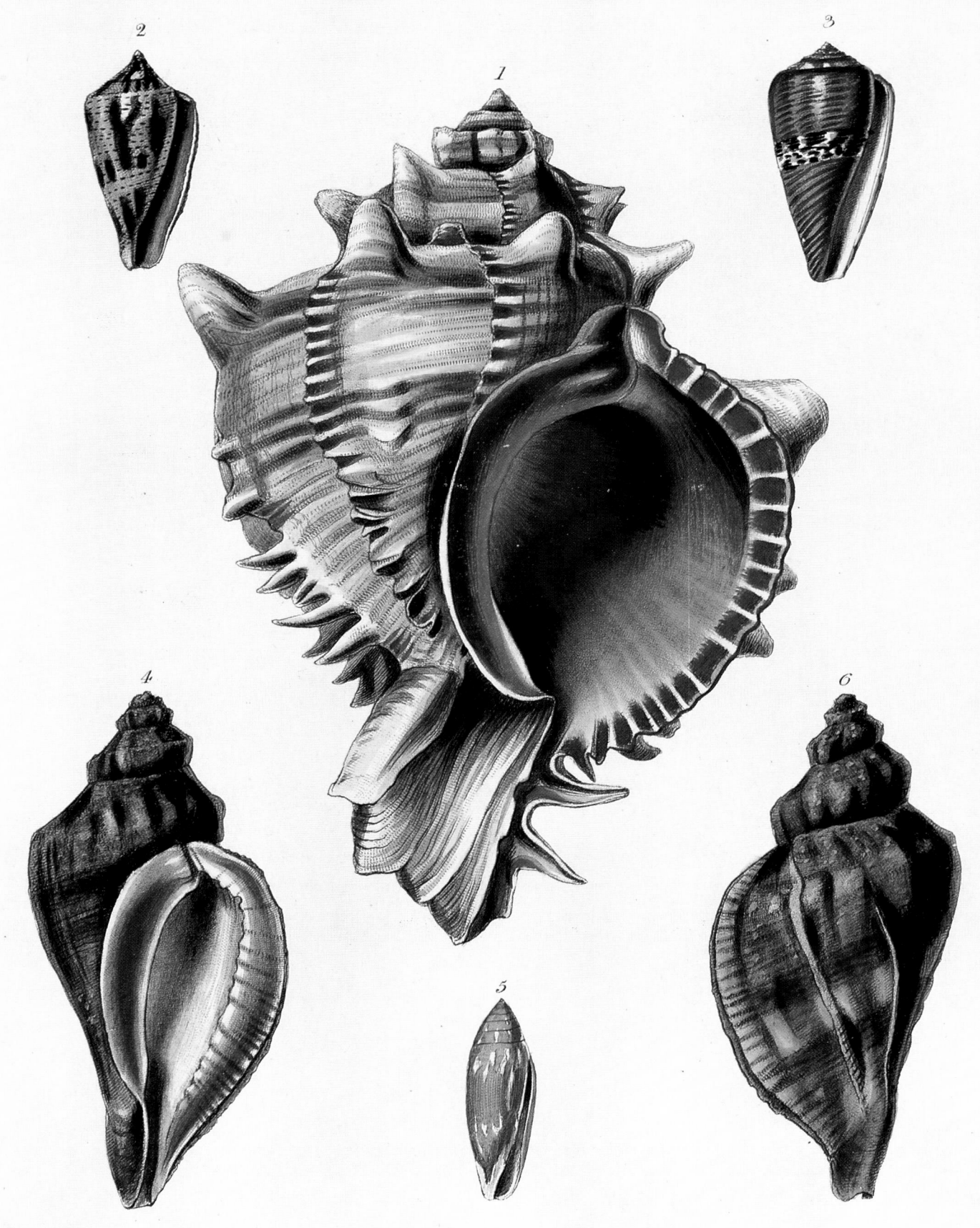

Regal Thorny-oyster and Others (c. 1841)

REGAL THORNY-OYSTER, *Spondylus regius* (top and bottom) and others. Colour-printed engraving by Victor after original drawings by Jean Gabriel Prêtre, colouring hand-finished by Gérard. pl. 20 from B. Delessert's *Recueil de Coquilles décrites par Lamarck et non encore figurées*, 1841–2. Size of plate 15½″ × 11½″.

Baron Benjamin Delessert, a businessman of Lyons, began collecting shells at about the age of thirty and as money was no object he could accumulate them with gay abandon. In 1840, with the purchase of the priceless shells of the Chevalier de Lamarck, a great pioneer of systematic conchology, Delessert's collection became one of the largest and most important ever made in Europe.

Among the baron's conchological treasures was a series of thorny oysters, *Spondylus*, said to be second to none in his day. The most celebrated specimen in the series was an exceptionally fine Regal Thorny-oyster, the shell shown at the bottom of this plate. It had had a curious – and scarcely credible – history before its acquisition by Delessert. Louis Claude Marie Richard, an eminent but impoverished botanist, had been offered the shell for a price way beyond his means. Unable to persuade the dealer to accept a lower price, Richard hurried home, collected up the domestic silver plate while his wife was not looking, replaced it with tin substitutes and sneaked back to the dealer who, having agreed to accept this unusual form of payment, parted with the coveted shell. Richard's wife, understandably, was furious and the shell became damaged as an indirect result of her fury. It was now the botanist's turn to be upset, and his distress caused Madame Richard to relent and forgive.

This must have been an exceptional example of the Regal Thorny-oyster, for Delessert reckoned it to be among the most precious of all the shells in his richly endowed cabinet. The species, still considered to be one of the outstanding members of a colourful genus, occurs on coral reefs in the Philippines and Japan.

J. G. Prêtre pinx.

Victor sculp.

Gérard color.

Bougeard imp.

Carrier Shells (1843)

Carrier Trochus, *Phorus onustus* (now Atlantic Carrier-shell, *Xenophora conchyliophora*) (centre) and others. Hand-coloured engraving by G.B. Sowerby (2nd), pl. 214 from Vol. 2 (1842–3) of L.A. Reeve's *Conchologia Systematica*, 1841–3. Size of plate 8½″ × 6″.

Lovell Augustus Reeve is best known for his monumental *Conchologia Iconica*, represented later in this selection by four plates. But his first substantial publication was *Conchologia Systematica*, a two-volume treatise describing and illustrating the principal groups of shells, its three hundred hand-coloured steel engravings being the work of George Brettingham Sowerby (2nd). The book had a limited scientific success but is still important because some species new to science were first described in it. Each of the two figures at the bottom of the plate, for instance, represents a species first given a scientific name by Reeve in this book. That on the left is now known as the Pallid Carrier-shell, *Xenophora pallidula*, that on the right as the Rough Carrier-shell, *Xenophora corrugata*.

Reeve also considered the central figure to represent a previously undescribed species, but it had been introduced to science more than sixty years earlier, as *Trochus conchyliophorus*, by Born in his book illustrating the conchological treasures of the Empress Maria Theresa. Because of its habit of cementing to itself shells and other objects, this West Indian species and its relatives are known popularly as carrier shells. Occasionally the Atlantic Carrier-shell attaches to itself such a weight of stones and coral that it is almost immobilized. On the other hand the Sunburst Carrier-shell, *Stellaria solaris*, represented here by the two top figures, does not disfigure itself in this way, the few small shells or fragments it acquires during the initial stages of its growth being unobtrusive.

Plate CCXIV.

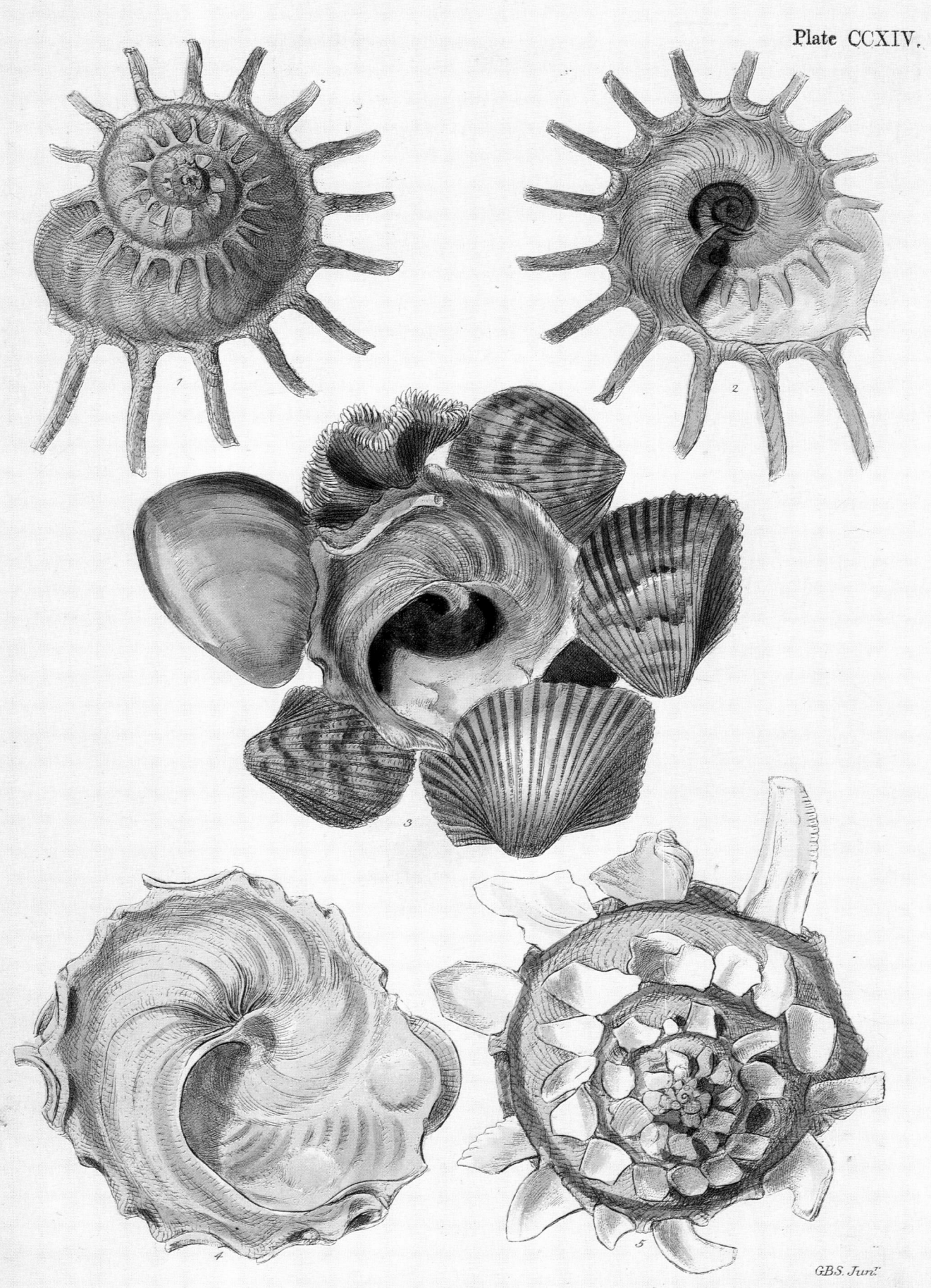

Sunrise Tellin (1843)

TELLINA RADIATA (Sunrise Tellin). Hand-coloured engraving by Victor from original drawings by Victoire Chenu, pl. 1 of *Tellina* from Part 18 (1843) of J.C. Chenu's *Illustrations Conchyliologiques &c*, 1842–53. Size of plate 16¼″ × 11½″.

After Baron Delessert had acquired the shells amassed by Prince Masséna, which included 50,000 shells formerly owned by the Chevalier de Lamarck, he had the largest shell collection ever formed by a private individual in France. Such a collection needed constant care and attention and so Delessert arranged for Louis Charles Kiener, who had worked for Prince Masséna, to act as curator. But, after a short time, Kiener took up an appointment at the Natural History Museum in Paris and Delessert had to find a new curator. As Prefect of Police, Delessert came to know Jean Charles Chenu, a military doctor and surgeon to the Paris municipal guard, and offered him the post. According to a catalogue Chenu published in 1844, Delessert's collection then contained about 25,000 species in three hundred genera and totalled 150,000 specimens.

Delessert himself had already published a sumptuous volume illustrating a selection of Lamarck's previously unfigured shells, one of its plates being reproduced earlier in this book, but with Chenu as his protégé he planned a series of illustrated monographs more magnificient than any seen before or since. The plan materialized as Chenu's masterpiece, the *Illustrations Conchyliologiques*, published between 1842 and 1853 in eighty-five parts, collected up into four lavishly illustrated folio volumes dedicated to his patron Delessert. But, as so often happens with grandiose schemes, it remained unfinished, as many of the plates were published without accompanying text. The project petered out after Delessert's death in 1847, although his collection, under Chenu's continuing curatorship, was the source of many illustrations for Kiener's *Species Général*. In 1869, Delessert's heirs, having tried vainly to get the Natural History Museum in Paris to take responsibility for his superb and historically important collection, presented it to the city of Geneva, where the family had strong ties. Chenu, an old soldier and by then infirm and with his eyesight failing, retired to the Hôtel des Invalides, where he died in November 1879.

Shown here are several colour varieties of the Sunrise Tellin, a shell common in the coral sands of the West Indies. As in many tellins, the back (or posterior end) of the shell is bent to the right, which helps the burrowing animal to assume its normal position, lying on its left side with its concave surface uppermost. The graceful lines and delicate colours of the Sunrise Tellin may never be portrayed more exquisitely than they are in this plate.

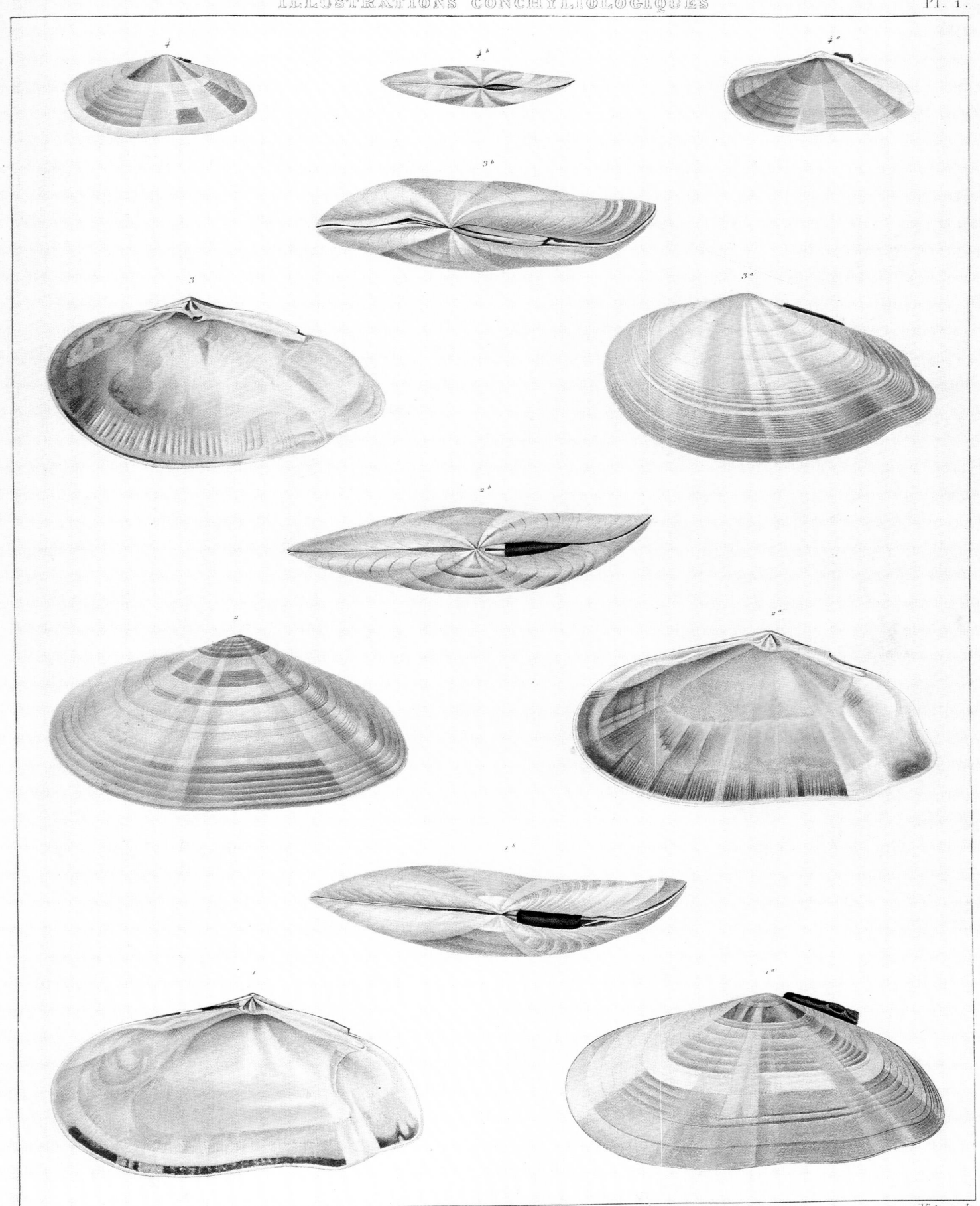

V. Chenu pinx.   N. Remond imp   Victor sculp.

G. TELLINA. Linné.

T. Radiata. Linné.

Queen Conch (1843)

STROMBUS GIGAS (Queen Conch). Engraving by Oudet from an original drawing by E.A. Prévost, hand-coloured by Gérard, pl. 2 of *Strombus* from Part 17 (1843) of J.C. Chenu's *Illustrations Conchyliologiques &c*, 1842–53. Size of plate 16¼" × 11½".

Among the most familiar of all sea shells, the Queen Conch was sufficiently large and attractive to deserve a plate to itself in Chenu's impressive four-volume work. Most of the plates in the *Illustrations Conchyliologiques* teem with figures which would have taken many hours to engrave. Alphonse Prévost, who provided the original drawing for this plate, must have found the Queen Conch a comparatively easy subject. P.L. Duclos, who wrote the *Strombus* monograph, says that, although the species is so plentiful in the West Indies, he had had the greatest difficulty obtaining one with the animal still inside it. He draws attention to the size of the animal, which is comparable to that of the shell, and says "its eyes are large, beautiful and brilliant". He could also have noticed that the right eye is at the end of a stalk which projects from the lower right-hand margin of the shell, as seen in this illustration, where there is a small embayment. This is a characteristic feature of shells in the family Strombidae.

Fishermen (and shell collectors) find the Queen Conch on the sandy bottoms of the sea in the West Indies, Bermuda and southern Florida. The animal is eaten and used as fish bait; the shell, too, has been marketed in various ways to satisfy the tourist trade. On rare occasions the Queen Conch (also known as the Pink Conch) has contained a pink pearl. This large and conspicuous mollusc has been so continuously over-fished that it now receives protection. Once a common sight as a doorstop or a garden ornament, it may yet become a rarity.

Pl. 2.

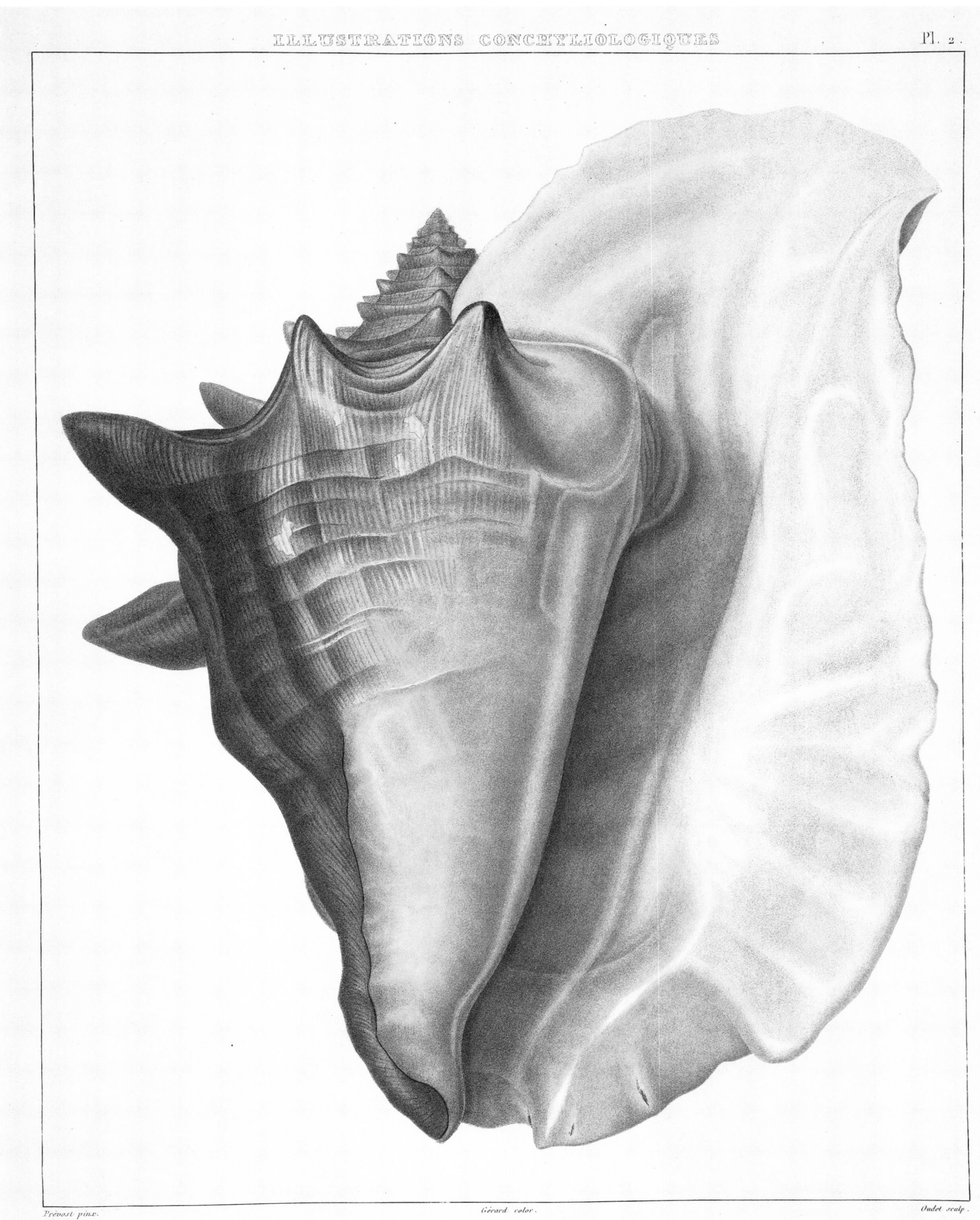

Prévost pinx. Gérard color. Oudet sculp.

G. STROMBUS. Linné

S. Gigas. Linné.

Green-streaked Helicostyla and Others (c. 1845)

HÉLICE MULTICOLORE, *Helix polychroa* (Green-streaked Helicostyla, *Helicostyla viridostriata*) (third row from top) and others. Hand-coloured engraving by Fournier from original drawings by J.G. Prêtre, pl. 19 of Mollusques from Vol. 3 of the *Atlas* to the *Dictionnaire Universel d'Histoire Naturelle* (edited by A.C.V.D. d'Orbigny), 1839–49. Size of plate 9″ × 5¼″.

This plate is from an encyclopaedia of natural history in which the subjects were described in alphabetical order. The complete work comprised sixteen volumes, the exquisite hand-coloured plates filling three of them. The illustrations, from original drawings by some of the leading natural-history artists in France, may explain its popularity. Jean Gabriel Prêtre supplied the drawings of shells. He seemed to have specialized in drawing shells to illustrate books published during the first half of the nineteenth century, but he is known to have produced lovely coloured drawings of birds and other animals.

Shown here are the shells of seven very different species of land snails from different parts of the globe. When the plate was published they were all known by French conchologists as Hélices (derived from *Helix*, the scientific name given to the genus to which they all, supposedly, belonged). Research since then has shown that they should be placed in other genera. The Green-streaked Helicostyla comes from the Philippines, lives in trees, and – uncommon among snails – has a bright-green shell. The distinctive species occupying the centre of the plate is the ground-dwelling Wagner's Pyramidsnail, *Oxychona pyramidella*, from Brazil. That shown at top right is the Ribboned Planispire, *Trachia vittata*, from south-eastern India and Sri Lanka where its empty shells are commonly seen scattered about on the ground.

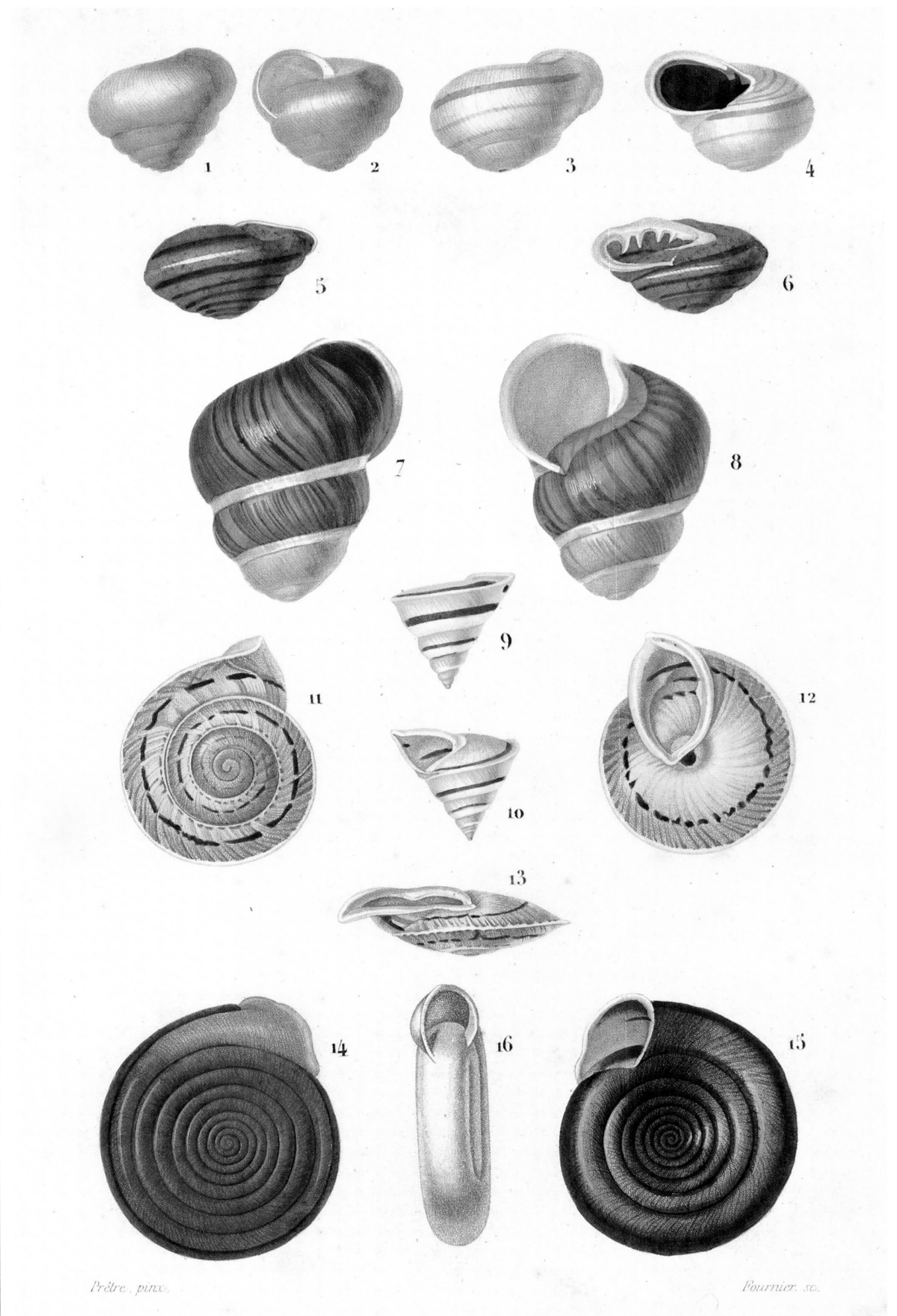

Prêtre, pinx.   Fournier, sc.

1.2. *Hélice trochiforme.* (Helix epistylium, Mull.) — 3.4. *Hélice macrostome.* (Helix vittata, Mull.)

5.6. *Hélice sinuée.* (Helix sinuata, Mull.) — 7.8. *Hélice multicolore.* (Helix polychroa, Swain.)

9.10. *Hélice Pyramidelle.* (Helix Pyramidella, Wagner) — 11.12.13. *Hélice de Lister.* (Helix Listeriana, Gray.)

14.15.16. *Hélice polygire* (Helix polygyrata, Born.)

Follau, imp.

Worm Shells (1846)

Vermet de Péron, *Vermetus peronii* (now Patchwork Worm-shell, *Tripsycha centiquadra*) (bottom) and others. Hand-coloured engraving by Cain from original drawings by Juliette Alberti, pl. 11 from the *Atlas* (1846) to the *Voyage autour du Monde sur . . . la Vénus, pendant . . . 1836–39 . . . par A. du Petit-Thouars &c*, 1840–64. Size of plate 16″ × 10¾″.

During the first half of the nineteenth century, the French government sponsored several voyages of exploration and research. Like most of the vessels used for these purposes, the *Vénus*, which was at sea from 1836 to 1839, called at island groups in the Pacific and at various places along the western coasts of North and South America. Natural history was an important part of the scientific programme, and a large collection of biological specimens, including molluscs and their shells, was brought back to Paris to be studied by specialists there. Scientific reports on the main groups of animals were prepared and published, Achille Valenciennes being responsible for that dealing with molluscs.

It is difficult to accept that the contorted tubes shown here are the shells of molluscs, impossible to regard them individually as eye-catching, but the impact of those shown in the bottom figure is immediate. The towering mass springing up from the surface of an old, worn shell of the Great Eastern Pacific Conch, *Strombus galeatus*, is more like a Gothic architectural extravaganza than a conglomeration of natural objects. Each of the two circular figures above it is an operculum, a thin, corneous plug sealing the entrance to each tube. The text to accompany the plates prepared for Valenciennes's report was never published, so we have no information about the shells illustrated in them. The Patchwork Worm-shell comes from the west coast of South America and the other worm shells portrayed here may also have come from that coast.

Peint par Melle J. Alberti.   Dirigé par Borromée.   Gravé par Cain.

1. LE VERMET A ÉCHIQUIER. *VERMETUS CENTIQUADRUS* (Val.)   2. LE VERMET DES PINTADINES. *VERMETUS MARGARITARUM.* (Nob.)

3. LE VERMET DE PÉRON. *VERMETUS PERONII.* (Nob.)

Gide Editeur.   Imp.e de Bougeard.

True Labyrinth-snail and other Snails (1846)

LABYRINTH-SCHNIRCKELSCHNECKE, *Helix labyrinthus* (now True Labyrinth-snail, *Lampadion otis*) (centre) and other land shells. Hand-coloured engraving, pl. 2 of L. Pfeiffer's "Die Schnirckelschnecken (Gattung *Helix*)" from Part 12 (1841–1906) of Vol. 1 of H.C. Küster's edition of F.H.W. Martini and J.H. Chemnitz's *Systematisches Conchylien-Cabinet &c*, 1837–1920. Size of plate 10¼″ × 7½″.

In 1837 Heinrich Carl Küster began to publish an enlarged edition of Martini and Chemnitz's *Conchylien-Cabinet*, the great encyclopaedia of shells published in Nuremberg during the second half of the previous century. Some of the figures published in the first edition reappear in the second, but although that is true of only one figure on this plate there is a distinctly eighteenth-century feeling about all the figures, especially when they are compared with those being published at about the same time in French and British encyclopaedic works on shells. Many specialists, including Louis Pfeiffer, a leading German authority on land shells, helped bring Küster's work to a successful conclusion, but progress was slow. The last part did not appear until 1920, more than eighty years after the first, by which time a total of 3,373 plates had appeared, most of them hand coloured, and accompanied by thousands of text pages. This was a mammoth task, but still many hundreds of species were left undescribed and unillustrated; there were just too many of them.

The centre of the plate is occupied by the True Labyrinth-snail, *Lampadion otis*, from Panama and Colombia, a species remarkable for the strong and convoluted barriers it develops within the aperture of its shell. The function of these barriers is to prevent insects and other predators getting into the shell while allowing the soft animal inside to venture out. The other illustrations represent tropical snails noteworthy for their large size, colouring and pattern.

Cowry Helmets (1848)

THIN CASSIS, *Cassis tenuis* (now Galapagos Cowry-helmet, *Cypraecassis tenuis*) (three larger) and CONTRACTED HELMET, *Cassis coarctata* (now Contracted Cowry-helmet, *Cypraecassis coarctata*) (bottom). Hand-coloured lithograph by G.B. Sowerby (2nd), pl. 6 of L.A. Reeve's "Monograph of the genus *Cassis*" (1848) from Vol. 5 of his *Conchologia Iconica or Illustrations of the Shells of Molluscous Animals &c*, 1843–78. Size of plate 11″ × 8½″.

When Lovell Reeve began to publish an extensive picture-book of shells in the middle of the nineteenth century he started with at least three important advantages: boundless energy, his position as a publisher and his friendship with the foremost shell collector of the age, Hugh Cuming. In 1843 he published the first of many monographs which comprise his *Conchologia Iconica*, using Cuming's collection as his principal source of illustrative material. He continued publishing the monographs until 1865, the year of his death (and Cuming's), when his illustrator, George Brettingham Sowerby (2nd), took over responsibility for them.

The monograph on *Cassis*, like most of the monographs, also used shells from collections other than Cuming's. Speaking of the Contracted Cowry-helmet, for instance, Reeve says, "For the magnificent specimen here represented, which is of unusually large size, I am indebted to the choice collection of Miss Saul." This was a reference to Jane Saul, who died in 1905 and whose fine collection is now in the Museum of Zoology in the University of Cambridge. But Hugh Cuming is the only collector honoured with an engraved portrait in the book. Without his collection, the *Conchologia Iconica* would never have extended to twenty bulky volumes.

13. a.

13. b.

14.

13. c.

Sowerby, del. et lith.

Reeve, Benham & Reeve, imp.

Areola Babylon and Murex Shells (1848)

EBURNA AREOLATA (now Areola Babylon, *Babylonia areolata*) (centre) and Murex Shells. Hand-coloured lithograph by G.B. Sowerby (2nd), pl. 8 of A. Adams and L.A. Reeve's "Mollusca" from part 3 (1848) of A. Adams's *The Zoology of the Voyage of H.M.S. Samarang &c*, 1848–50. Size of plate 10″ × 7¾″.

From 1843 to 1846 Sir Edward Belcher commanded the *Samarang* during a voyage to the Far East. Among those on board was the young ship's surgeon Arthur Adams, whose duties on the voyage included the study of the natural history of the places visited. To help him collect creatures from depths down to at least 136 fathoms, he used a dredge. The natural history report he edited upon his return paid particular attention to molluscs and their shells, conchology being a particular enthusiasm of his.

Adams was also an excellent artist and he made many coloured drawings of the living molluscs he observed in the tropics. The central figure on this plate was based on one of these drawings and represents a living example of the Areola Babylon, dredged in the China Sea from a muddy bottom at a depth of fourteen fathoms. A noteworthy feature illustrated by this drawing is the way the pattern of coloured blotches on the body of the animal is reflected in the pattern on the shell. "It is extremely rare to find any sort of concordance between the colouring of a mollusk and its shell," says Adams in the report he wrote with Lovell Reeve.

The *Samarang*'s itinerary encompassed the Philippines, but those islands failed to produce many molluscs previously unknown to science. The reason for this is given in the report. "With reference to the natural history of the Philippines, that sagacious and most indefatigable traveller, Hugh Cuming, Esq., had anticipated us in many points." During his four-year sojourn in the Philippine archipelago, Cuming, the "Prince of shell collectors", amassed so many previously undescribed shells that it was to be many years before significant additions were made to its molluscan fauna by others. Arthur Adams himself described many of Cuming's shells as new to science.

Giant Apple-snail and Others (1850)

AMPULLARIA CANALICULATA (now Giant Apple-snail, *Pomacea maculata* (two largest figures and bottom centre) and others. Hand-coloured engraving by C. Pierre from original drawings by J.G. Prêtre, pl. 3 of *Ampullaria* from Part 80 (1850) of J.C. Chenu's *Illustrations Conchyliologiques &c*, 1842–53. Size of plate 15½″ × 11½″.

The two figures at the centre of this plate represent the shell of the world's largest freshwater gastropod. Glossy and thin, it measures about six inches in length. The species lives in the Amazon Basin, which may explain why its shell was seldom seen in collections before the twentieth century; to carry such a fragile shell a long distance without breaking it must have been difficult when jungle travel was hazardous and uncertain. Even today few public museums and even fewer private collections can show large, perfect examples of it; hardly anyone thinks it worth the trouble to bring such an apparently valueless object out of the jungle. The Giant Apple-snail is not rare in nature, however, as Mr Tom Pain of London discovered in 1938. A leading authority on such shells, he collected it plentifully at Iquitos in Peru. He also noticed that the natives there were using the shells as receptacles in which to collect latex from rubber trees.

Apple snails are so named because of their globose shape and generally greenish colour, but some have a quite different appearance. In particular *Marisa cornuarietis*, shown at the top corners of the plate, is tightly coiled like a ram's horn. This species is abundant in streams and canals throughout tropical South America and the West Indies. In spite of the difference in shape between the shells of these two species, a study of their anatomy shows that they are closely related.

Prêtre pinx. N. Rémond imp. Pierre sculp.

G. AMPULLARIA. Lamarck.

1. A. Fasciata.
2. A. Dubia.
3. A. Canaliculata.

4. A. Fragilis.
5. A. Virens.
6. A. Roissii.

7. A. Canaliculata.

Chiragra Spider-conch (1851)

GOUTY PTEROCERA, *Pterocera chiragra* (now Chiragra Spider-conch, *Lambis chiragra*). Hand-coloured lithograph by G.B. Sowerby (2nd). pl. 2 of L.A. Reeve's "Monograph of the genus *Pterocera*" (1851) from Vol. 6 of his *Conchologia Iconica or Illustrations of the Shells of Molluscous Animals &c*, 1843–78. Size of plate 11″ × 8½″.

Where possible, Reeve tried to ensure that the figures of shells in his *Conchologica Iconica* were shown at the natural size. Sometimes this was not possible because the shell was either too large or too small. Seldom does the figure of a single shell occupy a plate to itself. When it does so, the result is usually aesthetically pleasing. Here the finger-like projections help to fill the available space admirably. Once again the shell illustrated, a fine example of a very common Indo-Pacific species, came from the bountiful cabinet of Hugh Cuming.

"This well-known species", says Reeve, "is chiefly remarkable from the widely-expanded, star-like arrangement of the claws." Not until the later stages of its growth, however, does it develop "claws", and the juvenile shell is often misidentified as something very different. But this is not the only way the Chiragra Spider-conch has deceived the unwary. Early in the twentieth century a detached "claw" from a shell of this species was picked up in the Gran Chaco region of South America by Andrew Pride. After studying it attentively, John Graham Kerr, Professor of Zoology at the University of Glasgow, concluded that it was the fang of an extinct venomous snake of gigantic proportions which he named *Bothrodon pridii* in a scientific article published in 1926. By analogy with the fangs of other known snakes, this one would have been a monster at least sixty feet long. A few years later the fragment of an innocuous seashell which had fooled a Scottish professor was exposed for what it was by a German palaeontologist. *Bothrodon pridii*, serpentine terror of the Gran Chaco, survives now only as a footnote in the literature of conchology and herpetology.

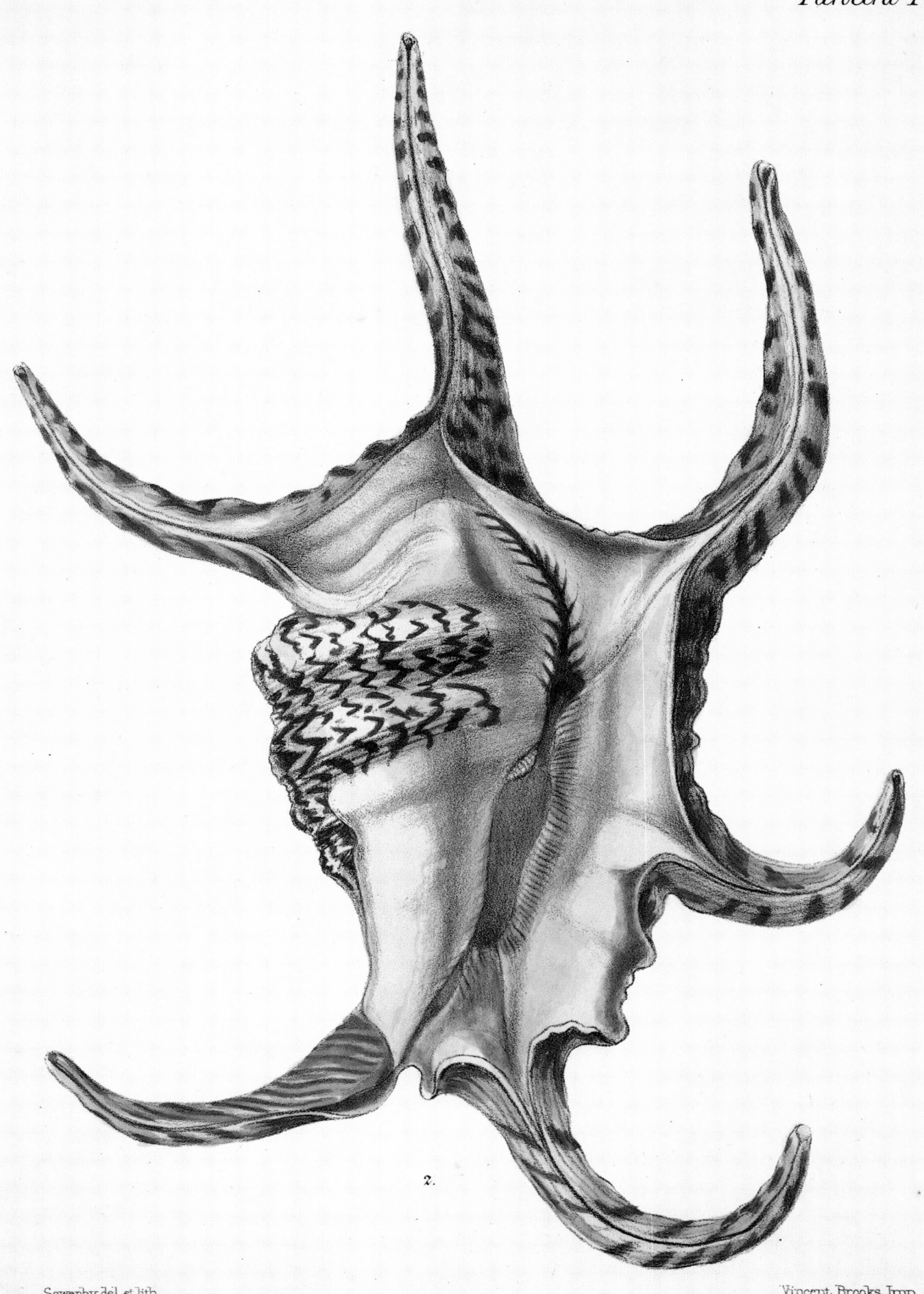

2.

Sowerby, del. et lith.

Vincent Brooks, Imp.

Most Beautiful Calocochlia (1851)

VERY BEAUTIFUL HELIX, *Helix pulcherrima* (now Most Beautiful Calocochlia, *Calocochlia pulcherrima*). Hand-coloured lithograph by G.B. Sowerby (2nd), pl. 6 of L.A. Reeve's "Monograph of the genus *Helix*" (1851–4) from Vol. 7 of his *Conchologia Iconica or Illustrations of the Shells of Molluscous Animals &c*, 1843–78. Size of plate 11″ × 8½″.

During his four-year sojourn in the Philippines, Hugh Cuming made a collection of land shells that vied in beauty and interest with the sea shells he had collected there. He used to send parties of schoolchildren into the woods to collect specimens for him and a liberal reward always awaited the discoverer of anything beautiful or rare – a practice which aroused the curiosity of the natives, who could not understand why anyone should give good money for such worthless objects. Noticing that they used an ash made of burnt snail shells to help them chew the betel-nut, their favourite vice, Cuming told them he was taking the shells home with him to serve a similar purpose. This explanation satisfied their curiosity. The Philippine land shells he brought back with him to England in 1840 dazzed the specialists and kept them busy for years describing new species.

The Most Beautiful Calocochlia, one of the many species never seen before outside of the Philippines, was described by George Brettingham Sowerby (1st) in 1841, but it was not until this plate appeared, ten years later, that collectors could see how wonderfully varied were the patterns displayed by a series of specimens. "Mr. Cuming collected this species in the island of Luzon", says Lovell Reeve in the description of this plate, "where he discovered it in all its varieties within a very limited area." He also points out that these ten figures fail to show its variations fully.

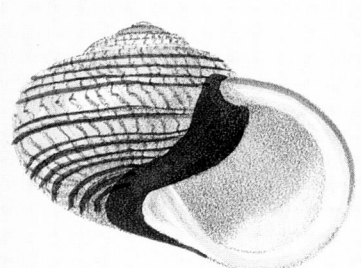

26. a.

26. b.

26. c.

26. d.

26. e.

26. f.

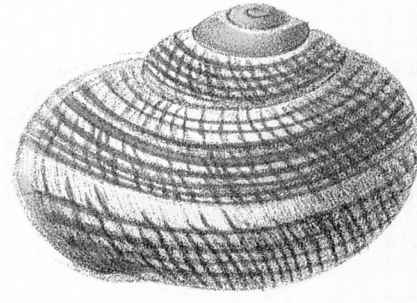

26. g.

26. h.

26. i.

26. k.

Sowerby, del et lith.

Reeve & Nichols, imp.

Umbrella Squid (1854)

LOLIDONE EUPHROSINA (now Umbrella Squid, *Histioteuthis bonnellii*). Hand-coloured lithograph by P. Davin from an original drawing by Philippe Gény, pl. 14 from A. Risso's *Mollusques Céphalopodes Vivants observés dans le Parage Méditerranéen du Comté de Nice*, 1854. Size of plate 15¼″ × 11½″.

This remarkable plate reflects something of the personality of the man in whose posthumous book it is such a striking feature. Born at Nice in 1777, Antoine Risso was in turn pharmacist, Professor of Physics and Natural History at the Lycée, and Professor of Chemistry and Botany at the Military School; he died at Nice in 1845, nine years before this plate was produced. Of his many works in natural history, the best-known is his five-volume *Histoire Naturelle des principales Productions de l'Europe Méridionale*, 1826–7. He was a prolific describer of new species – more than five hundred molluscs among them – but how good was his science? Jules René Bourguignat, in a critical review of Risso's non-marine molluscs published in 1861, observed that he had written something about almost every branch of natural history without having treated any one of them satisfactorily. "Among the bogus naturalists and among the publications of shallow scientific scholarship," says Bourguignat, "must be ranked Risso and all his works."

Whether that assessment is true or not, we make no apology for selecting a plate from Risso's *Céphalopodes Vivants*; the book is very rare and its plates are stunning. Issued in 1854 by the author's nephew, J.B. Risso, the book was possibly never offered for sale commercially. For this and for other good reasons, the new scientific names proposed in it have been almost totally ignored by the scientific community. The species illustrated as *Lolidone euphrosina* is believed to be the Umbrella Squid, but the configuration of its enlarged left eye is duplicated, erroneously, for the right eye as well. The arms and tentacles are arranged symmetrically, as in all the plates of this book, in a contrived artistic fashion. It is instructive to compare this plate with one showing the same species, from a work by Férrusac and Orbigny, reproduced earlier in this selection. Both images are visually arresting, but only one does justice to its subject.

Pl. XIV.

Fig. 4

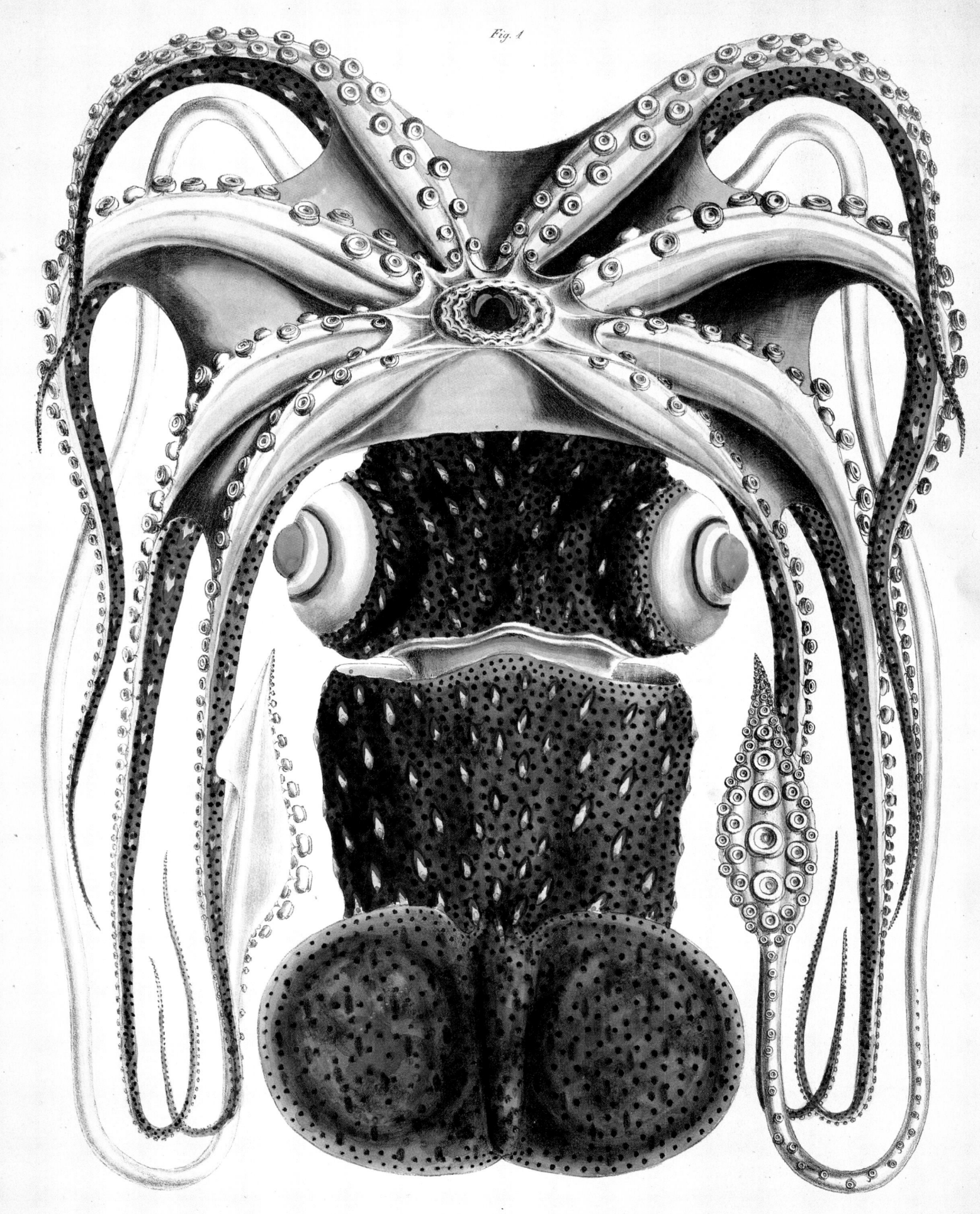

Lolidone **Euphrosina** Riss.

Phil. Gerny Del.

Nice, Lith. P. Davin et C.ᵉ

Freshwater Mussels (1856)

FRESHWATER MUSSELS. Hand-coloured engraving, probably by W. Wood (junior), pl. 21 from S. Hanley's *Illustrated and Descriptive Catalogue of Recent Bivalve Shells*, 1842–56. Size of plate 6¾″ × 4″.

As in the plate taken from William Wood's *Index Testaceologicus* of 1828 many similar figures of shells crowd into the confines of a small plate, which in each instance is reproduced here much enlarged. William Wood junior, a son of the author of the *Index*, may have executed the very accomplished engravings on this plate which, with others, forms a continuation of the *Index*.

The text to the *Catalogue of Recent Bivalve Shells* was by Sylvanus Charles Thorpe Hanley, a wealthy man who devoted the best years of his life – most of Victoria's reign – to collecting shells and studying them. Between the two world wars a large number of books about shells turned up in a small London warehouse and a conchologist bought most of them for a pittance. They had all come from Hanley's library which had been disposed of after he died in 1899. In every sense Hanley had treated them as working copies, dismembering the plates from some of them, cutting out the figures of shells and pasting them back into the books according to his fancy. The shell books he wrote himself, however, were illustrated conventionally.

All the figures on this plate are of freshwater mussels, many of them from river systems in North America where these large and often ponderous molluscs used to be abundant. Since Hanley's day, however, many species have been exploited, sometimes to the point of extinction, to satisfy the demand for products made from them, such as buttons and beads.

Sundial Shells (1863)

SOLARIUM MAXIMUM (now Giant Sundial, *Architectonica maxima*) (two largest) and others. Hand-coloured engraving by G.B. Sowerby (2nd), pl. 1 (= pl. 250 of the whole work) of S. Hanley's "Monograph of the Recent Species of the Genus *Solarium* of Lamarck" (1863) in Vol. 3 of G.B. Sowerby's *Thesaurus Conchyliorum*, 1842–87. Size of plate 7½″ × 5″.

During the nineteenth century, the Sowerby family worked as a team to produce a string of impressive books and lesser publications dealing with different natural objects but principally shells. For instance, the *Thesaurus Conchyliorum*, more than forty years in the making, was edited by three senior members of the family in succession and was illustrated with engravings prepared by them and coloured by junior members. But this was an ambitious undertaking and specialists were called upon to help out. One of those specialists was Sylvanus Charles Thorpe Hanley, who wrote the monograph from which this plate is taken.

Shown here are several sundial shells, a group characterized by shells each having a circular outline and an underside reminiscent of a winding staircase (hence the alternative name of winding-staircase shells which conchologists of an earlier age applied to them occasionally). Most of the engravings were taken from specimens then owned by the redoubtable Hugh Cuming, including the Giant Sundial, one of the larger species from the western Pacific. As it occurs widely in the Philippines, where Cuming collected shells extensively over a four-year period, it is possible that the specimen engraved was also collected by him.

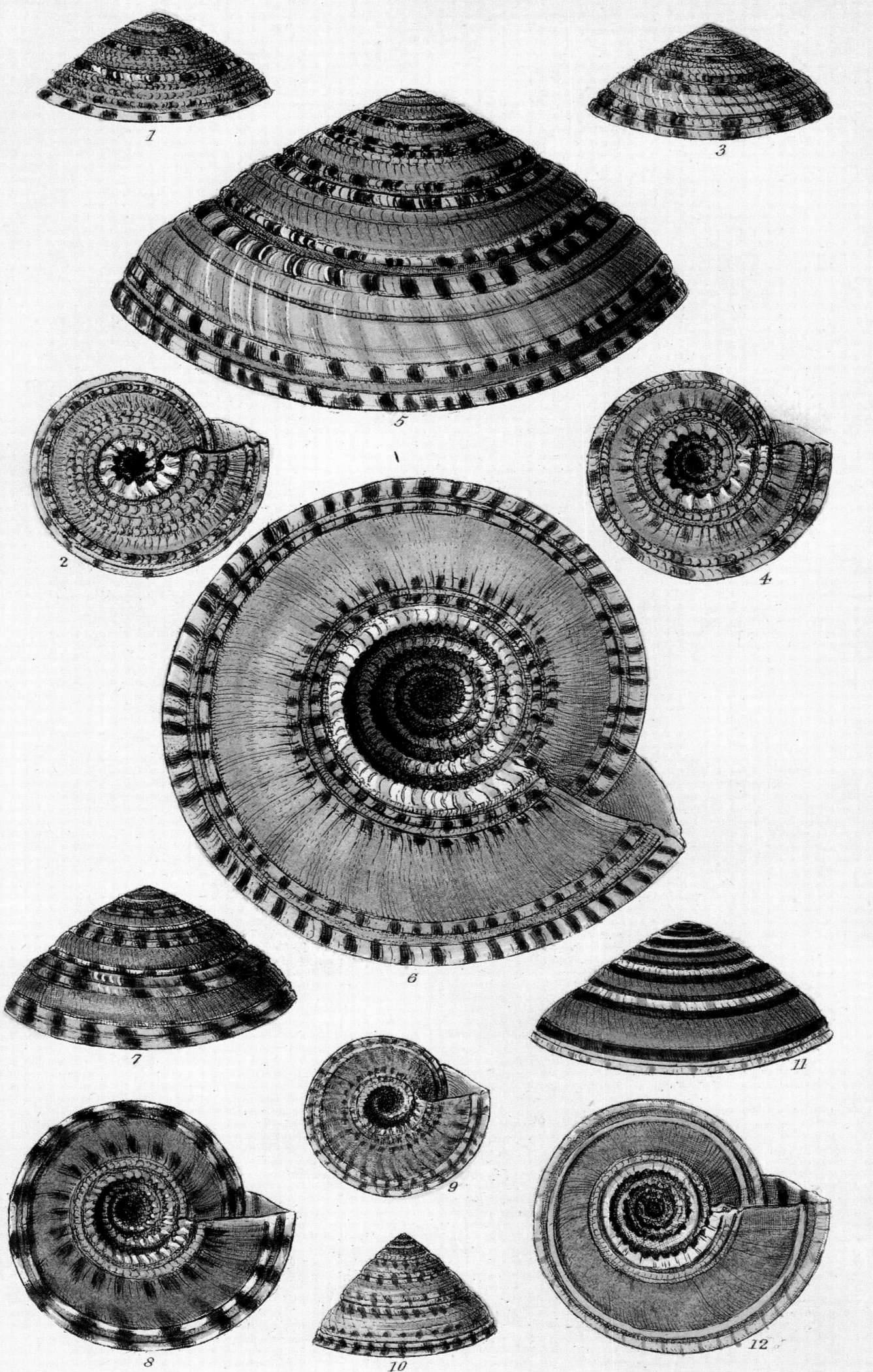

G.B.Sowerby.

Indian Sea-slugs (1864)

KALINGA ORNATA (centre and bottom left) and others. Hand-coloured lithograph by Edwin M. Williams from original drawings by native artists, pl. 32 of J. Alder and A. Hancock's "Notice of a collection of Nudibranchiate Mollusca made in India by Walter Elliot, Esq., with descriptions of several new Genera and Species", 1864, from Vol. 5 of the *Transactions of the Zoological Society of London*. Size of plate 12½" × 9¾".

Joshua Alder and Albany Hancock of Newcastle-upon-Tyne were keen naturalists, talented artists and lifelong friends. Their studies of the British nudibranchs, or sea-slugs, culminated in the *Monograph of the British Nudibranchiate Mollusca*, 1845–55, a folio-sized publication which brought them international recognition. Hancock's beautiful drawings, unsurpassed by any others of the same kind, were the definitive illustrations of the species and were much copied in other books. The presence of anatomical details makes these plates unsuitable for reproduction here, but copies of some of the sea-slug figures may be seen in the plate reproduced later in this book from Haeckel's *Kunstformen der Natur*. Instead, we commemorate Alder and Hancock by including a plate of sea-slugs from a late work published only three years before Alder's death.

Their illustrations of British sea-slugs stimulated search for these attractive animals in other seas. Knowledge of sea-slugs from the Indian Ocean had been limited to those discovered around island groups visited by the *Astrolabe* and other French exploratory vessels and by the British vessel *Samarang*. The coasts of continental India had not been explored. Inspired by Alder and Hancock, the medical officer to the Ceylon garrison, E.F. Kelaart, discovered more than fifty new species around that island. Simultaneously, the Scotsman Walter Elliot was using his position as Commissioner of the Northern Circars in the Madras Presidency to employ men to look for sea-slugs on rocky shores near Waltair. Elliot sent the preserved animals to Alder and Hancock for examination, together with beautiful and accurate drawings by native Hindu artists showing each species in the living state. He found forty-two species there, of which thirty were additional to those found by Kelaart, despite the proximity of Waltair to Ceylon (Sri Lanka). One of Elliot's new discoveries, *Kalinga ornata* may reach a length of eight inches and is shown life-size on the plate.

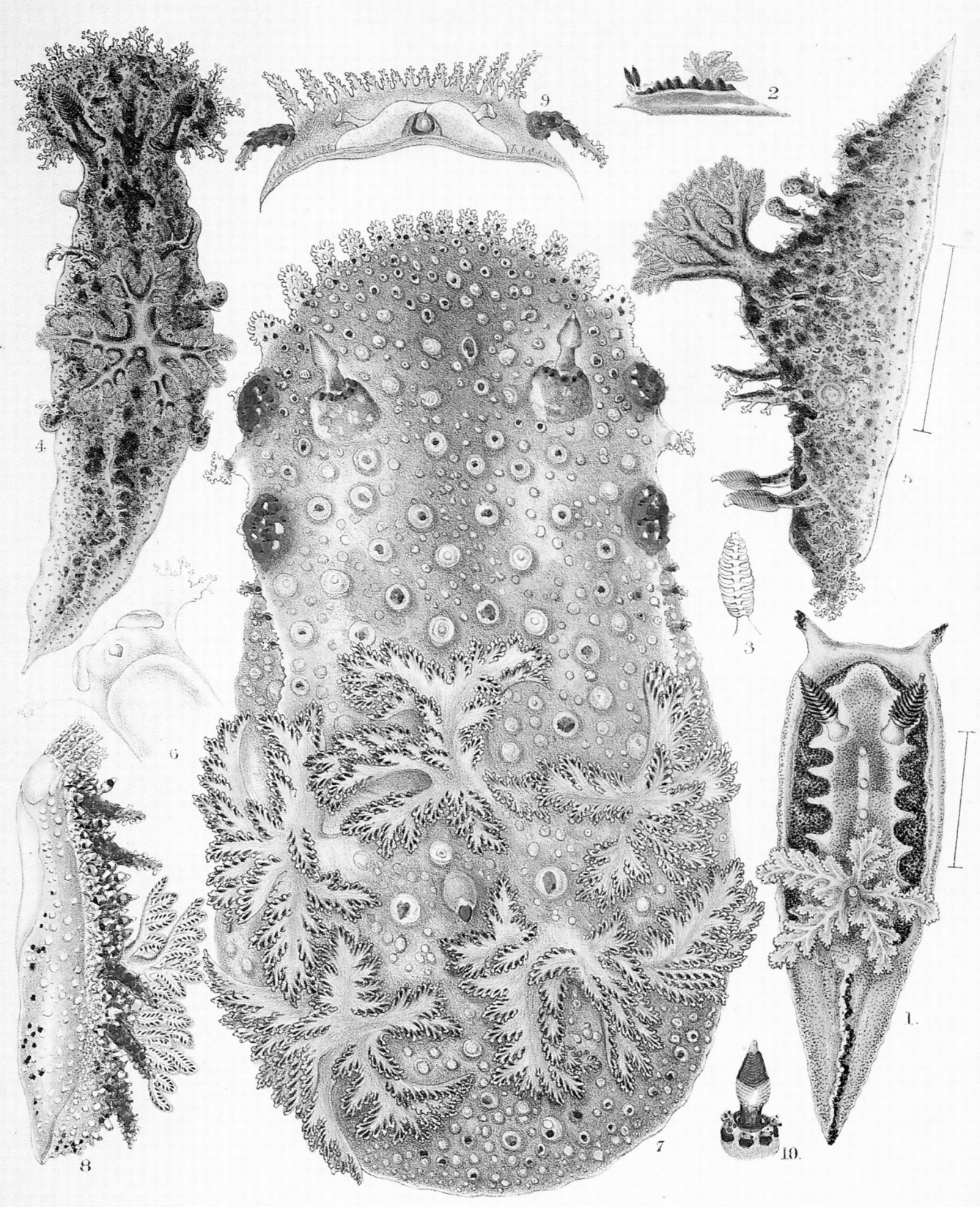

E.M.Williams, lith.

M & N. Hanhart, Imp.

Gold-mouthed Tun (1867)

DOLIUM JAPONICUM (now Gold-mouthed Tun, *Tonna luteostoma*). Coloured lithograph by W. Dunker, pl. 36 (1867) from his *Novitates Conchologicae: Mollusca Marina*, 1858–70. Size of plate 11½″ × 8¾″.

The German scientist Wilhelm Bernhard Rudolf Hadrian Dunker was an expert in geology, mineralogy and palaeontology, but he is remembered mostly for his contributions to conchology. He built up large collections of shells and fossils, and these were used to help make a firm foundation for knowledge of the German fauna. A skilled lithographic draughtsman, he often prepared the lithographs which illustrate his own publications, the one reproduced here being an excellent example of his work. It is one of many excellent hand-coloured lithographs from a serial publication about exotic shells written by him, and it captures the texture, sculpture and colouring of a shell which, though large, is thin and light. The delineation of two apparent breaks traversing its length, evidence of damage to its growing edge, suggests thinness and fragility. Similarly, the graduated but firm shading brings out the essential roundness of a shell which has been likened to a barrel. Lithographic technique has been used here so sensitively that you are convinced the shell would shatter if you dropped it. As it may be the size of a small football, there would be many pieces to pick up!

Dunker thought the shell belonged to a previously unknown species from Japanese waters, but it turned out to be the same as one described ten years earlier. The Gold-mouthed Tun is now known to occur in offshore waters from Japan to New Zealand but has never been common in collections. The specimen illustrated here had belonged to a fellow German, Friedrich Paetel, whose collection of shells came to be one of the largest in private hands in Europe. Ultimately the collections of both Paetel and Dunker were acquired by the Humboldt Museum in Berlin.

Dolium Japonicum Dkr.

Camp Pitar-venus (1868)

Lioconcha castrensis (Camp Pitar-venus). Coloured lithograph by Theodor Fischer, pl. 44 from Parts 14–15 (1868) of E. Römer's *Monographie der Molluskengattung* Venus, *Linné* (*Novitates Conchologicae*, Supplement 3), 1864–72. Size of plate 12¼″ × 9″.

The German city of Kassel is remembered for Denis Papin's first experiments with steam power and as the home of the brothers Grimm, but in the mid-nineteenth century it was not steamboats or fairy-tales that were in the air but conchology. Rudolph Philippi, Wilhelm Dunker and Louis Pfeiffer were all working there; and Eduard Römer, another conchologist, also made Kassel his base. Römer's colleagues were interested in marine and non-marine molluscs alike, but he was single-minded in his attachment to the study of marine bivalves. He wrote monographs on cockles (Cardiidae) and tellins (Tellinidae), but of all bivalve families he loved best the venus shells (Veneridae), as the two beautifully illustrated monographs he devoted to them show.

The first of these, depicting species of the genus *Dosinia*, appeared in 1862. The second, which was to have included all the remaining groups of the Veneridae, was a much larger undertaking than any attempted previously for these bivalves. In 1863, however, Lovell Reeve began to issue a series of monographs of the same family in the fourteenth volume of his heavyweight publication the *Conchologia Iconica*. Römer's timing was unfortunate, but the two works are very different. Reeve provided only brief descriptions and few figures of each species: Römer spared no details and often, as in this plate, included many figures showing variations of colour and pattern. Unfortunately, illness did not allow him to complete his work; the thirty-seventh part ends abruptly in the middle of a sentence. Two years later Römer died.

Both the common name and the scientific name of the Indo-Pacific species illustrated here refer to the conspicuous tent-like markings. Among bivalves this pattern is rarely seen other than on venus shells, but it is characteristic of some gastropod groups and is well seen on the Tent Olive, *Oliva porphyria*, and the Glory-of-the-Sea Cone, *Conus gloriamaris*, each portrayed elsewhere in this book.

L.L. castrensis Linné N. H.

Glandina Snails from Mexico (1870)

GLANDINA (now Glandina Snails, *Euglandina* species). Hand-coloured lithograph by Gustave Arnoul from original drawings by Bocourt, pl. 3 (1870) from the *Atlas* (1870–1902) of P. Fischer and H. Crosse's *Études sur les Mollusques Terrestres et Fluviatiles*, Part 7 of *Recherches Zoologiques* of the *Mission Scientifique au Mexique et dans l'Amérique Centrale*. Size of plate 13½″ × 9¾″.

The outstanding feature of this plate is the central figure showing a fully extended snail crawling along, dragging its pointed, four-inch shell behind it. Reproduced from an original drawing by Bocourt, it displays vivacity and aggression, attributes not normally associated with snails. Each of the other shells illustrated here would once have been similarly endowed, for all glandina snails are carnivorous and rapacious, especially for other snails. Related species have been introduced in various countries in an abortive attempt to control invasions of African achatina snails, but they have caused the extinction of several local species instead. Glandina snails have also been observed to turn cannibal.

The larger species occur in southern parts of the United States, Mexico and southwards to Ecuador. This plate, showing species occurring in Mexico, comes from an unfinished treatise on the land and freshwater molluscs of Mexico by two Frenchmen, Paul Henri Fischer and Joseph Charles Hippolyte Crosse, each of whom made important contributions to conchology. It shows that the French genius for producing high-quality natural history illustrations, in this instance using lithography and hand colouring, was still very much in evidence towards the close of the nineteenth century.

Arnoul del. et lith.　　　　　　　　　　　　　　　*Imp. Becquet à Paris.*

Glandina.

Adanson's Mangrove-oyster (1870)

PARASITIC OYSTER, *Ostraea parasitica* (now Adanson's Mangrove-oyster, *Crassostrea gasar*) (left) and others. Hand-coloured lithograph by G.B. Sowerby (2nd), pl. 2 of his "Monograph of *Ostraea*" (1870–1) from Vol. 18 of L.A. Reeve's *Conchologia Iconica or Illustrations of the Shells of Molluscous Animals &c*, 1843–78. Size of plate 10¾″ × 8¼″.

Oysters, unlike most bivalves, do not burrow but cement themselves to rocks or other shells or, in tropical waters, cluster on the stilt roots of mangroves. The surface to which they are attached influences their shape greatly, so separate populations of the same species may look dissimilar. This makes the identification of oysters very difficult. As their variability has become better understood, so the number of different kinds recognized by specialists has been reduced. Sowerby's monograph included eighty-seven oyster species but, even with the addition of those discovered since his time, the total accepted now is only thirty-six.

Michel Adanson, who was the first to recognize the oyster species shown here, spent five years studying the natural history of Senegal. His *Histoire Naturelle du Sénégal* was intended to be a comprehensive survey, but only the volume on molluscs was published, in 1757. It was the first attempt to classify shells by the animals they contained instead of by the external form of their shells alone. Among the West African species Adanson described was a three-inch-long oyster living on mangrove roots. He named it "Le Gasar" and reckoned its taste was equal to that of the best European oysters. Common in the River Gambia, the locality given for the specimens shown in Sowerby's lithograph, it may be the same species as the Tulip Oyster, *Crassostrea tulipa* (which itself may be merely a local race of the cosmopolitan Hooded Oyster, *Saccostrea cucullata*).

Adanson renounced the normal custom of giving to molluscs names which suggested that they resembled other objects, such as Tulip Oyster for a shell recalling a tulip with purple streaks on its blooms. Instead he preferred names which would be meaningless to the reader, such as "Gasar", "Codok" and "Dosin". According to the French naturalist Denys de Montfort, he had a novel way of coining these. He placed little wooden cylinders inscribed with letters of the alphabet in the barrel of a coffee-roaster. When the handle was turned and the door of the machine opened, random vowels and consonants spilled out which Adanson linked to form his barbarous names. As he also compiled lists of words from the local language, Wolof, it is equally possible that some of those words were adapted to his conchological purpose.

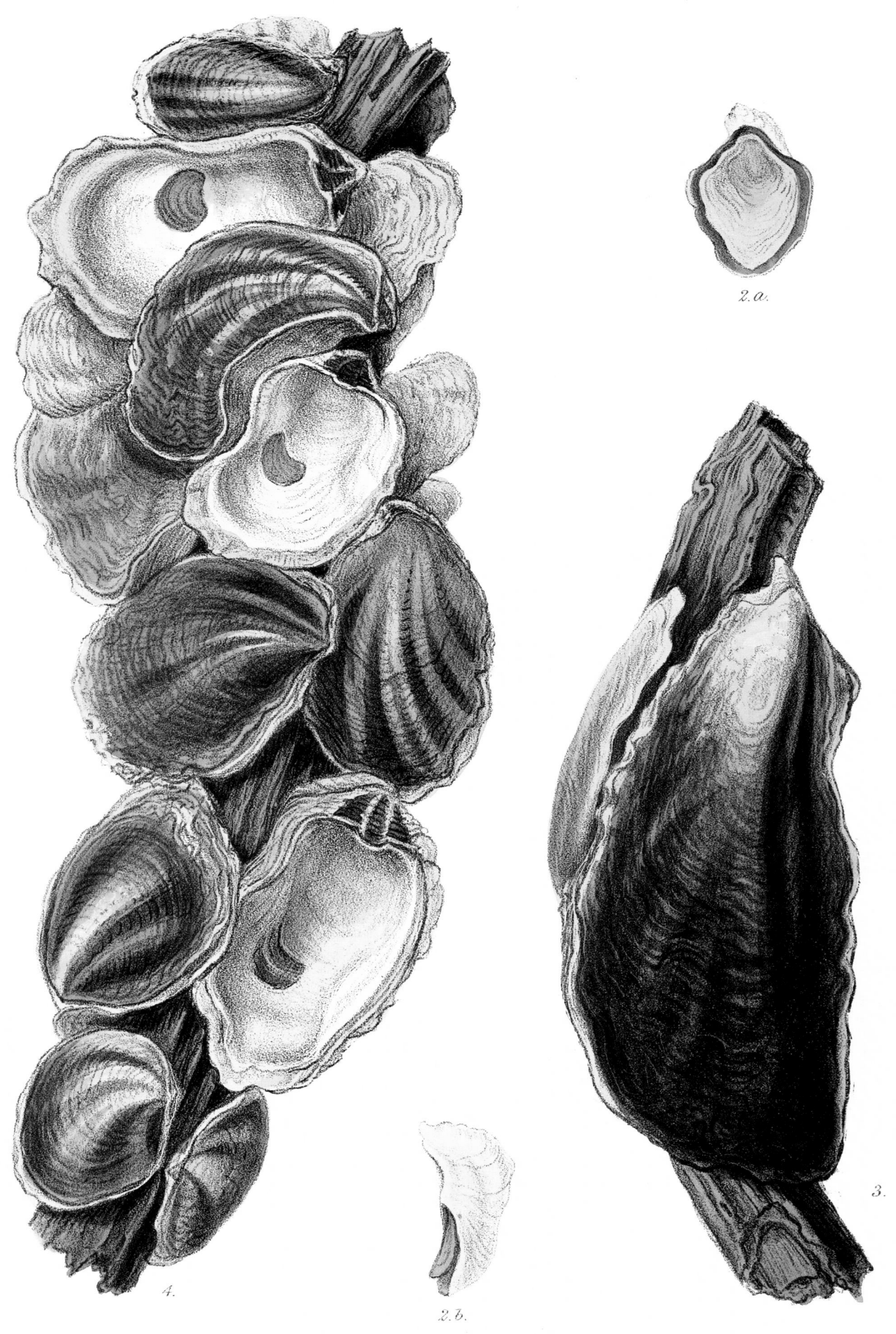

2. a.

4.

2. b.

3.

Sowerby, del. et lith.

Vincent Brooks, Day & Son Imp.

Saul's Triton (1871)

TRITON SAULIAE (now Saul's Triton, *Charonia sauliae*). Coloured lithograph by T. Fischer, pl. 2 from Part 2 (1871) of C.E. Lischke's *Japanische Meeres-Conchylien* (*Novitates Conchologicae*, Supplement 4), 1869–74. Size of plate 11½″ × 8¾″.

As we see elsewhere in this selection, the plates with the greatest impact are often those illustrating a single shell. This lithograph commands attention by being a faithful representation of a shell whose shape, pattern and colouring obviate the need for artistic elaboration. Although part of a scientific treatise, it would not look out of place in a book dealing with art objects, which helps explain why sea shells are collected so avidly, not least in Japan, the home of Saul's Triton. One of the many species Lovell Reeve introduced to science in the *Conchologia Iconica*, it was named after Miss Jane Saul, whose collection was often used by him to illustrate choice specimens in his monographs. Carl Emil Lischke's illustration is at least the equal of Reeve's.

The six-inch-long Saul's Triton occurs in the offshore waters of southern Japan, the home of so many attractive sea shells. A related species, the familiar Trumpet Triton, *Charonia tritonis*, is also found in the warm waters of southern Japan. For centuries this shell has been adapted for use as a trumpet, the sound being amplified within the shell so that it travels surprisingly long distances. The Japanese have used it for ceremonial and military purposes. The smaller Saul's Triton closely resembles three or four other species which live in parts of the globe remote from Japan, one of them, the Knobbed Triton, *Charonia lampas*, occurring as far away as the Mediterranean. Tritons brought up from deeper water often have more elongated shells and tend to be less colourful. Most of them, including Saul's Triton, are edible and in some parts of the world have been an important food source.

Triton Sauliae Reeve.

Two Japanese Cockles (1882)

CARDIUM BECHEI (now De la Beche's Cockle, *Nemocardium bechei*) (upper three figures) and *Cardium burchardi* (now Burchard's Cockle, *Acrosterigma burchardi*) (lower three figures). Coloured lithograph by T. Fischer, probably from original drawings by W. Dunker, pl. 15 from Dunker's *Index Molluscorum Maris Japonici &c*, (*Novitates Conchologicae*, Supplement 7), 1882. Size of plate 11¾" × 9".

In 1861, only seven years after Matthew Perry had negotiated the treaty which opened Japan to Western influence, Wilhelm Dunker published the first European book about Japanese marine shells, his *Mollusca Japonica*. This was followed by a steady stream of publications describing the wealth of new shells being discovered in Japanese waters, the most notable being Lischke's *Japanische Meeres-Conchylien*, 1869–74. In 1882 Dunker had enough new material to publish his compendious and well-illustrated *Index Molluscorum Maris Japonici*. Most of his lithographs show assortments of several species, but the plate selected here shows just two different kinds of cockle.

Arthur Adams and Lovell Reeve had already illustrated De la Beche's Cockle in the *Zoology of the Voyage of H.M.S. Samarang*, the *Samarang* having found some single valves of this handsome species near the island of Borneo. The shell portrayed here came from a Japanese collection and was the only complete specimen known at the time. In 1847 Reeve had named it after Sir Henry De la Beche, then Director of the Ordnance Survey and President of the Geological Society. Although no longer rare in collections, De la Beche's Cockle, which ranges from southern Japan to New South Wales, remains one of the most attractive in its family.

Burchard's Cockle was first described by Dunker from specimens found at Sagami Bay, a famous shelling locality on the south-east coast of Japan and one of the few places where this uniquely Japanese species lives. Dunker dedicated not only this species but his whole book to Wilhelm Burchard, headmaster of Bükeburg high school and an ardent beetle collector, who provided him with many rare shells to illustrate.

Tab. XV.

1

2

3

4

5

6

Ex offic. lithogr. Theodori Fischer.

Common Whelk Varieties (1886)

BUCCINUM UNDATUM (Common Whelk) and varieties. Coloured engraving by T. Fischer from original drawings by W. Kobelt, pl. 17 from Part 5 (1886) of Vol. 1 of Kobelt's *Iconographie der schalentragenden Europäischen-Meeresconchylien*, 1883–1908. Size of plate 9″ × 7″.

Like several nineteenth-century conchologists, Wilhelm Kobelt was an excellent draughtsman. He supplied the original drawings for many of the illustrations which accompany his books and shorter articles. One of his more ambitious projects was a four-volume account of the marine shelled molluscs of European seas, with illustrations of many of the species, including their varieties. The Common Whelk, *Buccinum undatum*, is one of the more variable gastropod molluscs of those seas, and here we see an example of the typical form (top left) together with some of its extreme varieties.

It is easy to understand why Lovell Reeve had regarded the variety shown at the bottom corners as a distinct species (he called it *Buccinum pyramidale*, in allusion to its shape). In the first half of the nineteenth century, conchologists such as Reeve did not appreciate that the shells of certain species could vary according to the nature of their environment. Furthermore, he was not alone in deriving satisfaction from describing innumerable so-called new species based on shells which differed from the typical forms. That is why many species have each been given more than one scientific name. In his many publications, Kobelt, who had been influenced by the ideas of Darwin, showed how variable were the shells of certain species. His conscientious studies helped resolve many problems of identification and classification which had hindered the study of molluscs, especially those of Europe and Asia, up to his day.

Kobelt del.   Artist. Anst. v. Th. Fischer, Cassel.

1–6. Buccinum undatum L.

Ponderous Orthalicus and Others (1893)

ORTALICHUS PONDEROSUS (now Ponderous Orthalicus, *Orthalicus ponderosus*) (bottom row, except right-hand figure) and others. Hand-coloured lithograph by Edward Wilson from original drawings by Eugen Duval, pl. 11 of E. von Marten's *Terrestrial and Fluviatile Mollusca* (1890–1901) from F.D. Godman and O. Salvin's *Biologia Centrali-Americana &c.* Zoology, 1879–1915. Size of plate 12¼″ × 10½″.

Between 1879 and 1915 Frederick DuCane Godman and Osbert Salvin masterminded and paid for the production of a monumental work on the zoology, botany and archaeology of Central America. Published in sixty-three quarto volumes and illustrated with 1,677 plates, 900 of them coloured, the *Biologia Centrali-Americana* was based on the incredibly rich and varied collections assembled by Godman and Salvin – 52,000 bird skins and more than 30,000 butterflies and moths testify to their industry – and it remains the most comprehensive work on the natural history of the region. Carl Eduard von Martens of Berlin, one of the most outstanding conchologists Germany has ever produced, studied the non-marine molluscs. This plate comes from the bulky volume containing the results of his studies.

The boldly striped members of the genus *Orthalicus* are among the more conspicuous snails of Central (and South) America. There are many species and countless colour forms of these large, elongate snails, most of which live communally on the trunks of trees. Some species are very common, some rare, a few from remote, mountainous areas being collectors' items. The Ponderous Orthalicus, with a two-and-a-half-inch shell, comes from the west coast of Mexico, where it is widely distributed.

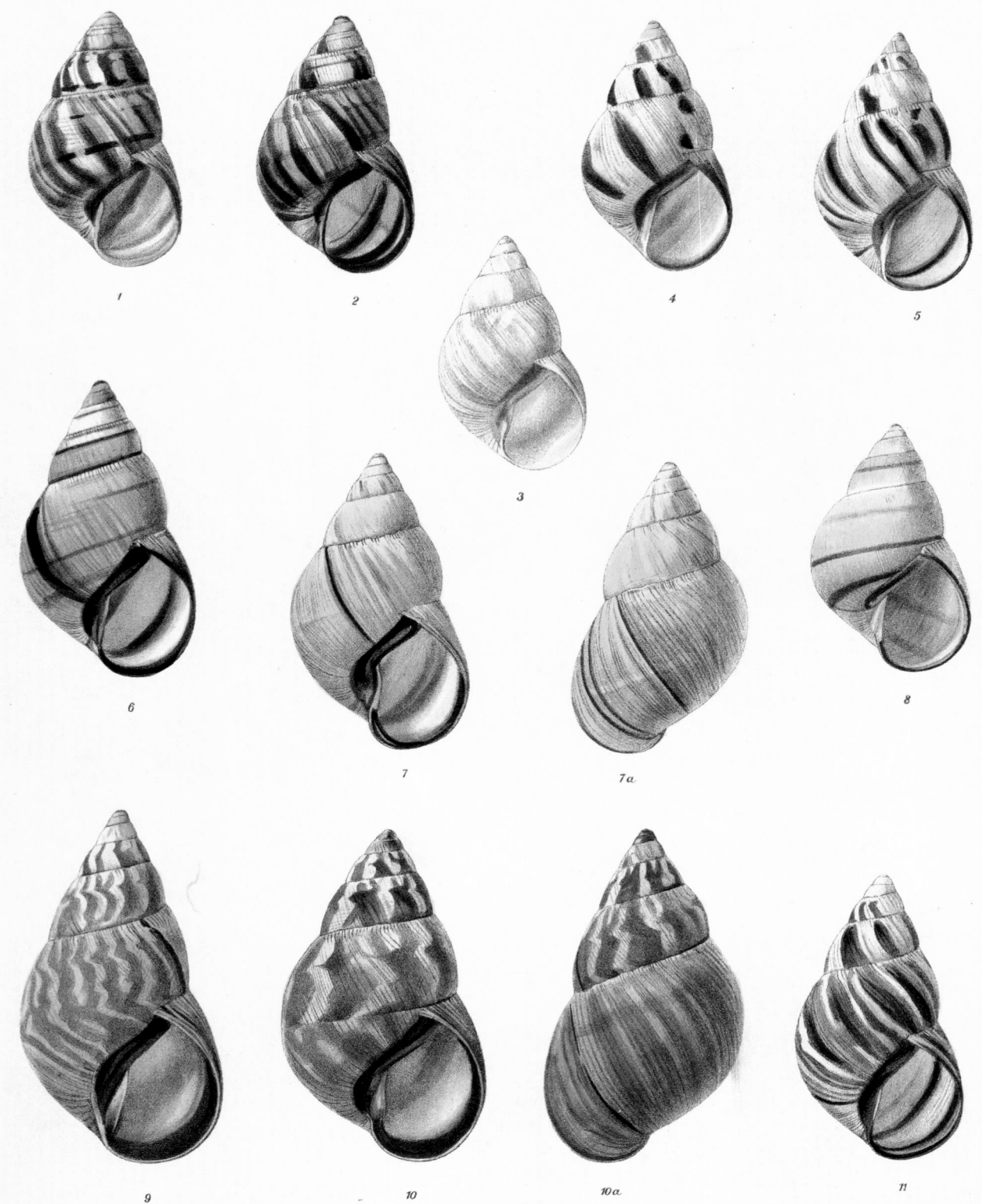

1-3   ORTALICHUS MACLURÆ.   8   ORTALICHUS TRICINCTUS.
4,5   „   BOUCARDI.   9,10,10a   „   PONDEROSUS.
6,7,7a   „   MELANOCHILUS.   11   „   BOUCARDI, *var*

Eug. Duval del.   Edwin Wilson. Cambridge.

British Sea-slugs (1904)

AEOLIS CORONATA (now Crowned Aeolis, *Facelina coronata*) (top right) and others. Chromolithograph by A. Giltsch. pl. 43 from Part 5 (1904) of E. Haeckel's *Kunstformen der Natur*, 1899–1904. Size of plate 11″ × 7¾″.

Ernst Haeckel discovered about four thousand new forms of marine life, many of them microscopic and obtained from the ocean depths. The physical structure of living creatures fascinated him and careful drawings of their beautiful or bizarre forms accompanied his published descriptions of them. But the philosophical aspects of evolution intrigued him more. He had even reconstructed Pithecanthropus, the supposed "missing link" between man and apes, before any fossils of it had been found.

He was also involved, although inadvertently, with another kind of "missing link". It had long been predicted that the simplest forms of life would be found in the deep sea. When, in mud samples from the Atlantic, Thomas Henry Huxley discovered a jelly-like material which seemed to behave like a primitive organism, he believed he had discovered something which closed the gap between living creatures and inanimate substance. He honoured Haeckel by naming it *Bathybius haeckelii*. Certain that *Bathybius* represented the origin of life itself, Haeckel "embraced this god-child with an enthusiasm surpassing that of its true parent". The *Challenger* deep-sea expedition found the same material in abundance, but it proved to be no more than a by-product of the mud and the alcohol preservative. Huxley received the sad news with dignity and admitted his mistake. Haeckel never mentioned *Bathybius* again. Instead, a crusader to the last, he set out to show the unity of Science and Art.

Haeckel considered that the beauty of most lower forms of life far excelled all man-made art and resolved to reveal this beauty to nature lovers and art lovers alike. Between 1899 and 1904 he issued ten portfolios, each containing ten plates, which comprise his *Kunstformen der Natur* (Art-forms in Nature). The illustrations, largely derived from Haeckel's own original drawings, are lifelike and many are arranged in stunning and almost surreal designs in which Art and Science do indeed combine. In this plate, however, the artist, Adolf Giltsch, has captured the individual beauty and graceful movement of a group of sea-slugs in a more conventional manner. These figures are largely based on those by Albany Hancock published in *A Monograph of the British Nudibranchiate Mollusca*, 1845–55.

Nudibranchia. — Nacktkiemen-Schnecken.

Alpine slugs (1910)

LIMAX MAXIMUS (Great Grey Slug). Chromolithograph by Werner & Winter from original drawings from life by H. Simroth, pl. 23 of Simroth's "Nacktschneckenstudien in den Südalpen", 1910, from Vol. 32 of *Abhandlungen der Senckenbergischen Naturforschenden Gesellschaft*. Size of plate 9½″ × 7¼″.

Wilhelm Kobelt was one of Germany's most celebrated conchologists, with a prodigious output of major publications to which he contributed both illustrations and text. For the second edition of the *Systematisches Conchylien-Cabinet* alone he drew the figures for more than nine hundred plates. In 1910 the Senckenberg Society for Nature Study brought out a commemorative volume, or Festschrift, to celebrate Kobelt's seventieth birthday, its frontispiece portraying his dignified features accentuated by his flowing white hair and beard. Many well-known conchologists contributed to the volume, but pride of place was given to an article by the master himself on the non-marine molluscs of north-east Africa, illustrated with eleven of his own lithographs.

One of the contributors to the Festschrift was Heinrich Simroth, who had a particular interest in land-slugs. He was intrigued by the marvellous patterns and colours, ranging from black to white through vivid red, bright yellow, grey and brown, exhibited by the large keeled slugs of the mountain forests of the Italian Alps. The plate reproduced here shows a selection of these varieties, one of which was even said to mimic the Asp Viper, *Vipera aspis*. In this article Simroth concluded that they were merely varieties of the widely distributed Great Grey Slug, *Limax maximus*. Some of the larger and more colourful of these slugs, which may reach over a foot in length, are now believed to be varieties of the Ash-black Slug, *Limax cinereoniger*, a name reflecting the normally more sombre hues found in British specimens. Simroth supposed that the rich and elaborate pigmentation was useful to these creatures in some way, but the reason for it has never been satisfactorily explained.

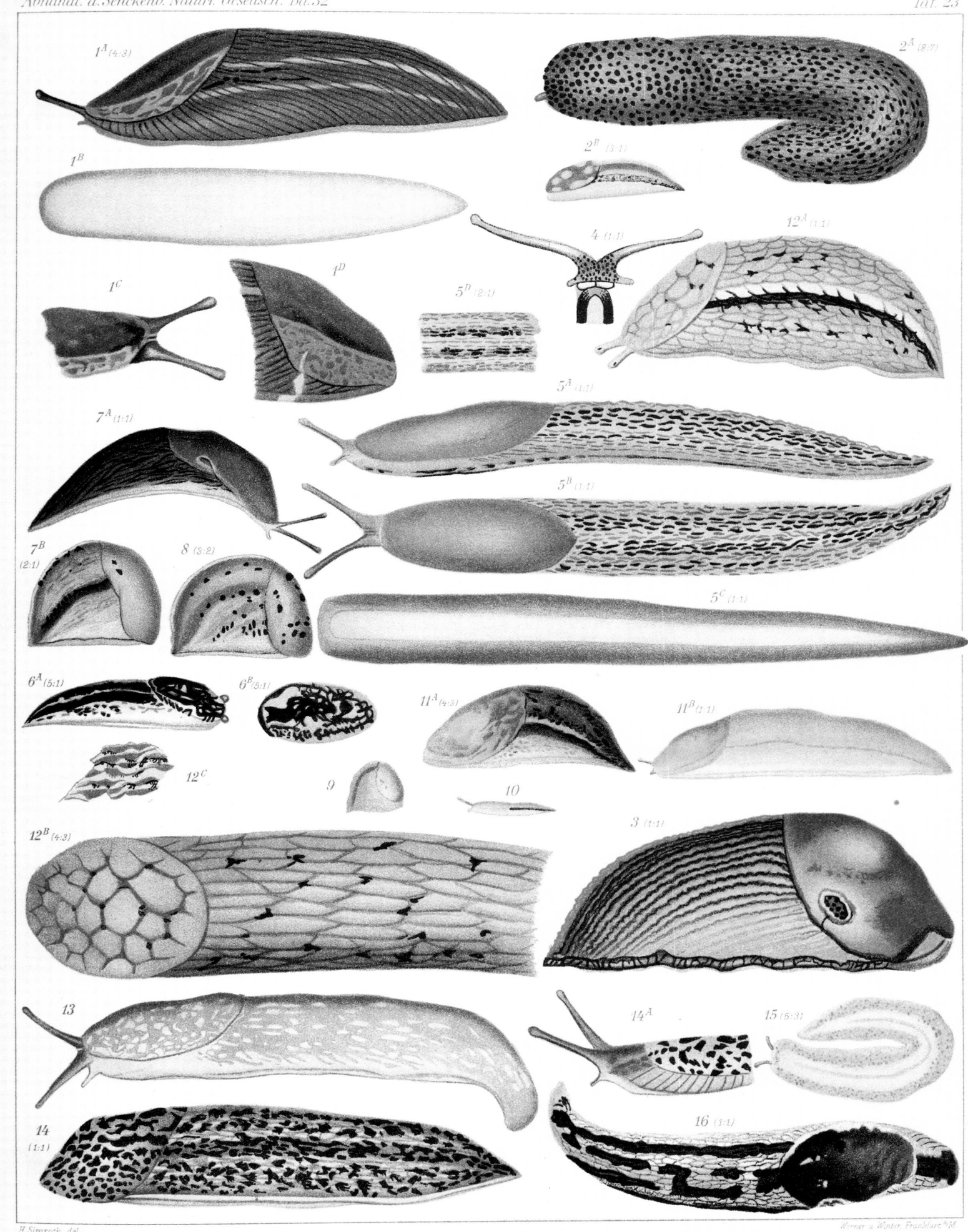

H.Simroth del.

Werner u. Winter, Frankfurt a. M.

H. Simroth: Südalpine Nacktschnecken

Rough Periwinkle Varieties (1912)

Littorina saxatilis (Rough Periwinkle) varieties. Chromolithograph, pl. 9 of P. Dautzenberg and H. Fischer's *Mollusques provenant des Campagnes de l'Hirondelle et des la Princesse-Alice dans les Mers du Nord*, from Part 37 of *Résultats de Campagnes scientifiques du Prince de Monaco*, 1912. Size of plate 13¾″ × 10½″.

Albert Honoré Charles Grimaldi, Prince Albert I of Monaco, satisfied his scientific curiosity and great love of the sea by active involvement in oceanographical research. In 1885 he transformed the little sailing-yacht *Hirondelle* into a floating laboratory, and by 1898 he had fitted out the 1400-tonne steam yacht *Princesse Alice II* with winches and steel cable for deep-sea explorations. Prince Albert himself acted as navigator and commander of a long series of voyages. The scientific results of these were published between 1889 and 1950 in 109 sumptuously produced monographs. One of the fattest of these described molluscs collected from off Newfoundland by the *Hirondelle* in 1887 and from around Norway and Spitzbergen by the *Princesse Alice II* between 1898 and 1907. It was written by two of France's ablest conchologists, Philippe Dautzenberg and Henri Fischer. Each was well placed to study such material; Fischer occupied the Chair of Malacology at the Natural History Museum in Paris, while Dautzenberg had a large collection rich in growth series and variations of colour and form. These large suites of shells from many different localities enabled them to study variation in many of the Arctic species obtained by Prince Albert.

In their report, Dautzenberg and Fischer painstakingly investigated the different forms of the Rough Periwinkle. The disconcerning variability of this common species had caused many forms to be named which might be regarded as separate species – except for the occurrence of innumerable intermediate forms. Of the several varieties shown on this plate, however, not one was figured from material amassed by Prince Albert, nor even from material obtained in Arctic regions. Dautzenberg's collection provided all the shells illustrated. This admirable investigation is now recognized as a pioneering study of the variable species of periwinkle, the first of many which others have continued to this day.

MOLLUSQUES DES MERS DU NORD

Liguus Tree-snails (1912)

Liguus Tree-snails from Florida. Three-coloured-half-tone print from original hand-coloured drawings by H.A. Pilsbry, pl. 39 of Pilsbry's "Study of the Variation and Zoogeography of *Liguus* in Florida", 1912, from Vol. 15 of the *Journal of the Academy of Natural Sciences of Philadelphia*. Size of plate 13½″ × 10½″.

This plate not only illustrates some remarkable shells but also shows us an unexpected side to the career of a remarkable man, Henry Augustus Pilsbry. The most industrious American conchologist of his generation, Pilsbry described many hundreds of new species and almost single-handedly revolutionized the study of land snails and their classification. But he is not celebrated as a conchological artist, so it comes as a pleasant surprise to see that he was responsible for the coloured drawings from which this plate was prepared. The attractiveness of his subjects may well have inspired him to make this artistic statement.

The shiny and colourful tree snails of the genus *Liguus* occur in Cuba, Hispaniola and southern Florida, where they live on or close to trees growing in lime-rich environments. Although scientists and collectors have named some 160 so-called species and varieties, it is now agreed that these are mostly colour forms of only six different species. In Florida some sixty names have been given to colour forms of what is now regarded as a single species, *Liguus fasciatus*. Florida Tree-snails are associated especially with the Jamaica Dogwood and the Wild Tamarind tree. When not feeding, they often choose to rest in some of the higher branches of these trees, affixing themselves with hardened mucus. Knowledgeable collectors used to dislodge them with a long telescopic pole to the end of which was attached a small can (although they no longer do so in conservation areas, such as the Everglades National Park, where the snails receive total protection). During the twentieth century, astronomical numbers were removed by collectors, whose depredations, together with the damage inflicted by building developments, hurricanes and animal predators, have annihilated some populations and threaten the continued survival of many others.

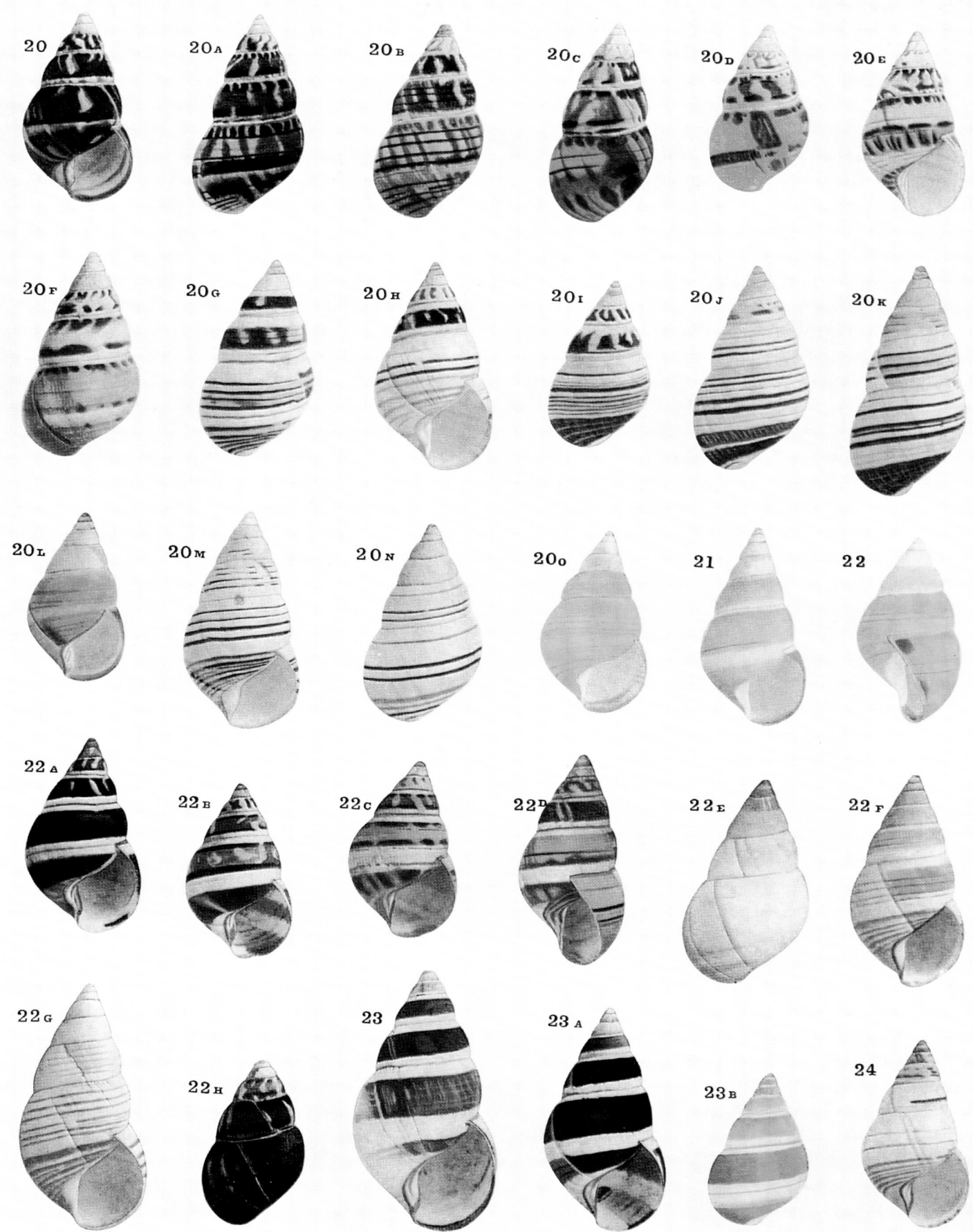

PILSBRY, PINX

PILSBRY: VARIATION AND ZOOGEOGRAPHY OF LIGUUS.

Japanese Woodcuts of Shells (1915)

JAPANESE SHELLS illustrated by woodcuts. Hand-coloured woodcuts by an unknown artist, pl. 25 from Part 2 (1915) of Y. Hirase's *Kai Sen Shu: One Thousand Kinds of Shells Existing in Japan*, 1914–21. Size of plate (double-page spread) 14″ × 9¾″.

The Japanese were writing about shells as long ago as the tenth century, but few of their writings published before the twentieth century are known in the West. It was Yoichiro Hirase, the leading shell collector in Japan for some years, who put his country on the conchological map with his publications, among which was an unusual book, *Kai Sen Shu*. Issued in four silk-bound volumes, it illustrates typical Japanese shells in a traditional Japanese manner. The plate reproduced here shows several common shells from Japanese waters.

Hirase's friends thought it strange he should have chosen the ancient wood cut method to illustrate his book, but he had an answer for them. "I have been no stranger to the elaborate elegance of lithography in colors," he says in a note printed in the book in English, a language he understood very well, "nor do I dislike the brilliant clearness of three-color printing; and yet this work being not wholly for the benefit of scientific studies, but rather for the purpose of reference for artists and technologists, and besides being intended to be distributed not only among our country-people, but also to the friends abroad who have the same interest in conchology as we do, I consulted about the printing with the master of the book-store 'Unsodo', Kyoto, an expert in printing, who gave warm sympathy and approval to my plan of printing with wood-cuts. This is why I have used the wood-cut art, which has been existing a long time in Kyoto, and has advanced to an excellent state of development. A great number of friends abroad congratulated us on the occasion of its issue, saying that they would appreciate the work as a rarity, since it, as a whole, represented an elaborate art peculiar to the Japanese." Hirase's friends were right, for *Kai Sen Shu* is unique among conchological publications and is highly prized by each fortunate owner of a copy.

INDEX